The Practical Handbook of
CAR CARE
and
REPAIR

By David N. Wenner

Fawcett Publications, Inc.
1515 Broadway
New York, New York 10036

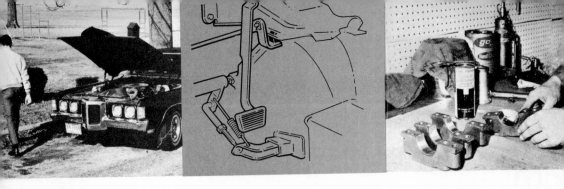

FRANK BOWERS: *Editor-in-Chief*

WILLIAM MIUCCIO: *Creative Director*

HAROLD E. PRICE: *Associate Director* • HERB JONAS: *Assistant Director*

JOSEPH C. PENELL: *Marketing Director*

CHRIS SCIARRINO: *Production Editor*

Editorial Staff: JOE CORONA, DAN BLUE, ELLENE SAUNDERS,
JULIA BETZ, LARRY N. WERLINE

Art Staff: MIKE GAYNOR, ALEX SANTIAGO, JOHN SELVAGGIO,
JOHN CERVASIO, JACK LA CERRA, MIKE MONTE, AL JETTER

How-To Art by Gene Thompson
Cover Color by the Author

THIRD PRINTING

Printed in U.S.A. by
FAWCETT PRINTING CORPORATION
Rockville, Maryland

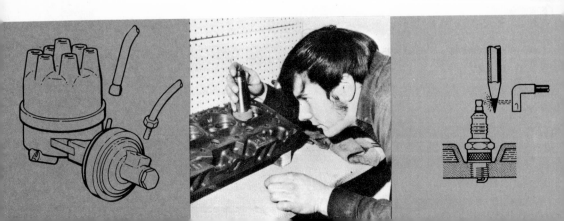

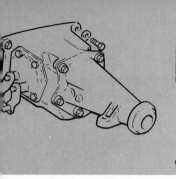

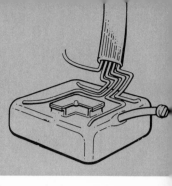

CONTENTS

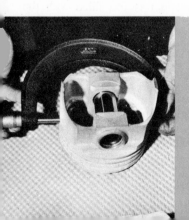
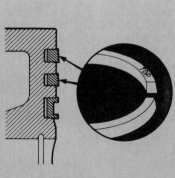

BREAK-IN TIME

Treat your new car right and
it will give fewer problems later on

The beauty of a brand new automobile is more than skin deep. But as in the case of a newborn baby, it often takes a little while before all the parts start working well together. No competent pediatrician would ever suggest weaning an infant on tabasco sauce, yet occasionally one hears a self-styled auto expert advising drivers to "shoot the hot stuff" with their cars from the moment they take delivery. The precision machining of auto parts has come a long way in the past two decades, but most new engines still have more tight spots than a prize Holstein in a training bra. It's the car owner's job to make sure that the fit improves as painlessly as possible.

KEEP COOL

The low-viscosity break-in oil supplied at the factory is supposed to prevent metal-to-metal contact where clearance between parts is minimal. Unfortunately, high operating temperatures not only make the mechanical components of a new car expand, thereby reducing clearances even further, but cause the low-grade shampoo in the crankcase to thin out quicker than a woolly worm caught walking on the railroad tracks. The new anti-smog gimmicks, incidently, contribute about as much to low underhood temperatures as a gallon of nitroglycerin and a five-pound hammer.

Although most car makers now suggest only modest break-in precautions, their seemingly cavalier attitude is usually tempered by some casual comment to the effect that "should anything unusual occur, it is advisable to stop immediately and contact the nearest Clunkmobile dealer." While their intentions are good, they lack the guts to say what they mean in plain language. What they're talking about are *unusual sounds and odors*—the kind produced by an engine that's getting ready to seize solidly as a watered martini in a polar explorer's canteen.

By the time a new car's temperature gauge says "hot," damage may already have been done. Unless it's hay fever season or your snoot is too filled with the fragrance of hops, the smell of overheated metal is about the best early warning system for detecting an engine that's getting tighter than a tax collector's smile. Remember, *it's never too late to stop for a cool-off*.

Allowing a new engine to reach normal operating temperature is fine, but just in case something *is* starting to get rubbed the wrong way, it's always a good idea to

Heat and hard use can be very damaging to new machinery. The very best place to break in your new car is in open country where life and traffic keep moving slowly but steadily.

stop and "cool it" for fifteen or twenty minutes with the hood open after driving for an hour or so. If you keep pushing it, the microscopic lumps on pistons, bearings, and gear surfaces will not be worn off smoothly, but will weld together and tear out little chunks of metal. While initial damage may be almost invisible, it can cause weak spots and localized stresses that may eventually lead to cracked pistons, accelerated bearing wear, and burned valves.

THINK LUBRICATION

When starting your new car, run the engine for a few moments before you bang it into gear and burn out for the ka-

rate studio. This will give the oil a chance to circulate around moving parts for greater protection when working loads are finally applied. Break-in oil is fine, but don't leave it in for more than 200-300 miles. Drive the car for a while to warm up the oil, then get the drain plug out almost before the wheels have stopped rolling. Yank the filter too. This is the only way you can be sure that metal particles worn from the new parts and shavings accidentally dropped into the crankcase by the night sweeper at the factory will have half a chance of draining out. Another oil change at about the 1,000-mile mark should get any grit and gubbins left behind on the first try.

Open country is the best place to break

Terrible piston galling got started in this engine before the machining marks even got worn off the piston skirt. This is what happens when you keep pushing a hot engine.

Valves lead a hard life in today's engines. Tight clearances and inadequate lubrication caused galling on stem. Bright specks on facing are welded-on bits of the valve seat.

Oil additives, especially designed and recommended for aiding break-in can be very beneficial in preventing metal-to-metal rub between new, tight-clearanced parts.

in your new car—another discouraging bit of news for those who dwell in metropolitan areas. While you may not be lucky enough to live in Pawnee Center, Kansas, you should at least be able to find a spot in the suburbs where traffic is relatively light and you can keep your car moving. New cars that are extra tight and tough to break in are as rare today as cast iron pistons and wooden wheels, but if you happen to get one, try a can of a friction-reducing oil additive. It will help prevent scuffed pistons and cylinder surfaces even though the beneficial effects of such "snake oil" is shamefully short-lived.

VALVES ARE IMPORTANT

Cars that need valve grinds at low mileage are often victims of improper break-in. The sports car buyer who decides to see whether the engine really "red-lines" in fourth gear on his very first stint behind the wheel is a prime candidate for early valve trouble. So is the fellow who elects to try cut-rate "regular" gasoline when his engine requires "premium."

New cars should be broken in on *leaded gasoline* because it has a lubricating

Have the wheel alignment checked on your new car also. Unless it is correct from the very beginning you will never get the full use from the tires that should be possible.

When the weather is warm and your car is brand new it's wise to take an occasional walk in the park while the engine cools off. Raising the hood will allow heat to escape.

effect on the valve and seat facings. Most auto makers are delivering cars with the tanks filled with leaded fuel for this reason, even though the engines have been designed for operation on unleaded gas. Other manufacturers recommend that leaded fuel be used periodically during the car's life since the effect of the lead is residual. It's wise to stick to leaded gasoline for at least the first couple of tankfuls and to save the low-lead stuff for the day when your engine has finally "gotten it all together."

GEARS

Some car makers have stopped putting drain plugs in the transmission and differential housings, but it's still a good idea to drain the original gear oil out after the first few thousand miles even if it means using a suction pump. Metal particles worn from new gear and bearing surfaces won't do a bit of good if they're left floating around in the oil. Replace the oil with the correct grade and remember that limited slip differentials require a special lubricant. Get it from your car dealer or a speed shop if the village grease monkey doesn't have it in stock. If you're going to

be towing a trailer or heavy boat early in a car's life (heaven forbid!) make sure that you read what the owner's manual says about heavy-duty service.

WHEELS AND SUSPENSION

Everything from the four patches of rubber rolling over the highway to the last inch of your new car's springs must be gradually accustomed to the constant flexing and load fluctuation produced by driving. Stay off rough roads even if it means avoiding lovers' lane for the next six months. Uneven rail crossings and pot-holed city streets are bad too. There's more to breaking in a new car than babying its engine, so unless you want sagging springs, leaking shocks, worn-out tires and rattling suspension parts at 10,000 miles you'll be well advised to take it easy for the first 5,000.

Today's owner's manuals sometimes give drivers the impression that breaking a car in carefully is "old fashioned." And it might be—if everybody threw their cars away after only one year's use. But in an era when disposing of "dead" cars is a gigantic headache, "throwaway" automobiles are hardly a desirable means for reaching utopia.

It's not easy to restore the appearance of a car that has been neglected. Owners who are conscientious will take steps to preserve the finish and appearance from the time it's new.

APPEARANCE

Mechanical wizardry isn't required to keep your car looking great

There's more to owning a sharp-looking automobile than treating it to a weekly trip through the car wash. If you happen to be one of those pillars of American prosperity who trade for a new dreamboat every year, such care may seem more than adequate. But then, that type of person seldom reads past the first chapter in this type of book. We'll therefore assume that you intend to keep your car for two or three years and that you'll be smart enough to steer clear of one-year-old, one-owner cars when it comes time to trade.

START WITH THE FINISH

Early care of your car's finish is every bit as important as pampering the ma-

chinery. You've got to admit that driving a well cared for older car makes a much better impression than wheeling up with a new convertible that's marred by dents, dirt, missing chrome, and has more rattles than an all-skeleton rhumba band. Which category your automobile falls into largely depends on you.

Most cars now have acrylic lacquer paint jobs that should be waxed as soon as you take delivery.

The occasional import that's dressed up in enamel has usually spent enough time on the boat to make waxing safe too. In fact, such cars are usually held for shipment until their finish is dry enough to take the anti-corrosion wax that's liberally sprayed over them before the ocean voyage begins.

WASHING

Correct care for car finishes starts with a proper washing. One dumb trick that ruins more paint jobs than six years in a Jersey City parking lot is washing automobiles with water and *kerosene*. If there's any wax at all on the car, and if there's even a flicker of life left in its finish, kerosene and strong detergents are guaranteed to destroy them.

The stuff that leaves a sheen on kitchen floors will eventually leave an expanse of dull and rusted sheet metal on your car. Unfortunately, this is also true of the high-pressure hot water, steam-clean, and high-strength detergent baths used in commercial car washes. Unless you're so lazy that you actually prefer to lap up lager in front of the boob tube and leave car washing to the crew of former Ukrainian torturers employed at the corner Kwik-Kleen, there's a better way.

Plain cool water is best, but a mild soap made especially for washing cars is permissible on finishes that are soiled and not merely dusty. Hot water and dishpan stuff are "no-nos." Work with a bucket and a large, soft sponge. Rinse with cool running water, but never aim a strong spray directly against the finish. A garden hose without a nozzle is a good choice.

Although some "purists" shun the practice, baking soda dissolved in the wash water or applied directly to the car's finish will soften and remove bug spots with a bare minimum of rubbing. It's been alleged that even the mild abrasive quality of baking soda might reduce the shine on enamel, but it is likely that the additional rubbing needed to do the job without baking soda would be just as bad. When completely dissolved, baking soda has no abrasive quality at all and softens the insect remains strictly with its alkaline chemistry.

Don't wash your car in sunlight or while the metal is hot unless you want the finish to resemble the crockery in a greasy spoon diner. In fact, the only way to eliminate water spots completely is to wipe the car dry. A chamois skin is traditional, but soft cotton terry towels are impossible to beat. Never wipe car finishes with synthetic materials since they absorb water poorly and sometimes scratch the paint.

WAXING

All cars need waxing, but waxing is more than merely giving your car a shine.

Chrome polish alone is not good for taking care of brightwork trim. To protect the chrome and prevent rusting it is necessary to apply wax to freshly polished chrome.

Some waxes contain cleaners which will be able to remove small tar specks. However, larger blobs should be cleaned off with tar remover before waxing. Don't use gasoline.

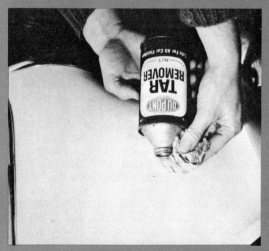

Removing the remains of splattered insects is the toughest part of washing your car in summertime. Applying baking soda to the bug spots will make them wash away easier.

A mixture of glycerine and talcum powder can be painted onto window gaskets or other rubber parts of the car's body to help keep their appearance, resist weathering.

Good wax also helps protect the finish from oxidation and the abrasion caused by flying dirt particles and hard-shelled bugs. To do the job right, you'll need something that does more than add a bit of superficial glitter.

Liquid waxes are no easier to apply by hand than soft paste-wax preparations and usually contain a lot less wax for the money. Hard waxes that require a great deal of rubbing aren't all that superior to paste waxes that have been formulated to rub off easily. Owners of small cars seldom gripe about hard-to-use waxes, but if you drive something with a hood the size of a pool table, anything that makes the job easier will doubtless be appreciated.

The finish should be thoroughly clean before applying any wax. The cleaners in most modern waxes will take care of small tar specks without trouble, but if the flanks of your trusty steed look as though half the paving material from the county roads of Tennessee has plastered itself onto them, you'd better spring for a can of tar remover. Some motorists dis-solve tar with gasoline, but this is far from beneficial to the car's finish.

If the paint has gotten duller than a wombat's gaze, precede the waxing with an application of body polish. Minor scratches or severe rough spots can often be erased with rubbing compound, but be careful not to rub right through the car's finish! Tar cleaner, polish, and rubbing compound remove wax. Unless you're preparing the car for a wax job, either wax the small areas that are treated or leave tar specks and poor paint alone.

Use a circular rubbing motion when applying wax. Don't employ a great deal of pressure. Let the chemical and abrasive cleaners in the wax do the work naturally. After the wax has dried it should be buffed off using the same kind of soft terry towels suggested for drying the car after washing. Power buffing is to be discouraged since it leaves whorls in the finish and can produce a reassuring shine even though it has burned your lovingly-applied wax job right off the car.

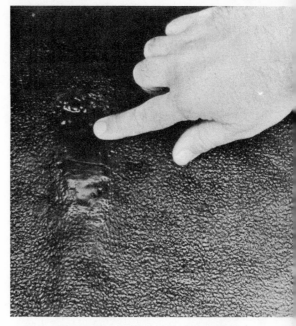

Cracked rubber parts and open joints in window gaskets can be sealed with liquid rubber. This will prevent air pollution from eating away at the rubber's interior.

Liquid rubber is also practical for making large repairs to such things as trunk mats. Place a piece of cloth behind the damaged area and fill the hole with liquid rubber.

CHROME AND TRIM

The plated parts and brightwork on your car need care too, but often the care they get is the wrong kind. Countless auto owners have scrubbed the bumpers and hubcaps of their cars with chrome polish only to have them rust just as quickly as those on their neighbor's car which have never been cleaned since the car was new. Chrome polish is great for shining things up, but you must remember that it leaves nothing behind except bare metal. After polishing, always apply a coat of wax. Harder, longer-lasting floor wax will protect automobile trim better in winter.

Aluminum must never be cleaned with chrome polish. It contains abrasives that will destroy annodized color finishes and gives a dull look to silvery aluminum trim. Make sure that any wax used on aluminum does not contain abrasive cleaners; most do. Even fine abrasives can impart a mottled appearance to annodized surfaces.

In most instances, loose trim can be re-placed by obtaining new clips and re-mounting it. Damaged trim must be re-placed, but if only the finish is bad it may be practical to have larger parts re-plated. Check with the speed shops in your area to find out where chroming can be done and how much it will cost to do the parts for your car.

RUBBER CARE

When "Boss" Kettering of General Motors made his well-known statement that the only difference between a new car and a junker was about six ounces of metal, it seems surprising that he over-looked the deterioration of rubber parts altogether. Most rattles, wind whistles, clattering suspensions, sloppy handling, and vibrating windows can be blamed on cracked, worn rubber parts.

Talcum powder is good for keeping trunk lids and door gaskets from sticking. It can also be rubbed into such parts as window gaskets to prevent aging and cracking. Unfortunately, it disappears

Sticking weather strips around doors and trunk lids soon begin tearing and leaking. Dusting their surfaces with talcum powder occasionally can prevent most such damage.

Tail lights with rusty reflectors not only keep your car from twinkling as it did when new but are also downright dangerous. Glue in aluminum foil to restore brightness.

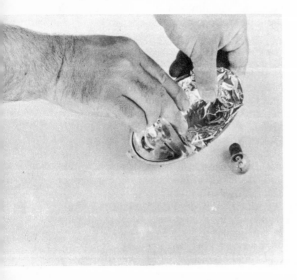

like a politician's promises the first time you encounter a rainstorm. Mixing the talcum into a thin paste with glycerine will help it stick and allow you to paint it on with a brush.

Grease and oil are very damaging to rubber and should be cleaned off immediately if they are accidently splattered onto tires or suspension bushings. Brake fluid is an effective agent for washing rubber and may be used to lubricate rubber parts that flex, turn, or twist while the car is in operation. Powered graphite is another good lubricant, but it's awkward to apply. It is best suited for use where rubber is in working contact with metal. Spray-on silicone lubricants are excellent for easing the operation of windows in their guides or in other locations where graphite might soil clothing and cause a mess. Engine belts should be lubricated with V-belt dressing.

RUBBER REPAIR

The first step toward repairing cracked, disintegrating rubber is to restore its protective exterior so that air pollution, grease, and other destructive agents can not penetrate to further damage its interior. Used car dealers often apply tire black, but this is more cosmetic than protective. Liquid rubber is better since it fills cracks, adheres permanently, and has properties similar to those of the original part. Scrub the damaged area with detergent and allow it to dry, then spread on liquid rubber. Some formulas permit thinning with solvents so that the compound can be painted on. Consult the directions on the tube. Rubber strips and gaskets that have come loose from the body can be put back with trim cement, another readily-available item in auto supply stores.

UTILITY AREAS

Trunks and station wagon cargo areas can also profit from regular clean-ups. Rubber floor mats that are scuffed or cracked should be cleaned and painted with tire dressing. Holes and tears in mats can be repaired easily by placing a patch of heavy cloth coated with liquid rubber under the opening and filling the hole with

A greasy engine is just as ugly as a muddy fender. It can also be a fire trap. Give the engine compartment an occasional bath with spray degreaser followed by a water rinse.

additional liquid rubber. It's available in both black and white, and mixing the two or adding dry pigment to the white can help approximate the mat's color.

MECHANICAL AREAS

Occasionally car owners who keep their machines scrupulously washed and waxed, will neglect underhood cleanliness completely. A dirty engine not only looks bad, it's dangerous. All it takes is a minor fuel leak and one tiny spark to start a blaze that can't be switched off with the ignition key. An annual cleaning with spray-on degreaser is insurance against such calamities.

There's not much to the job. Merely take off the air cleaner and plug the carb throat and any hoses or tubes that lead into the air cleaner. Cover the distributor and alternator with plastic bags and spray on the degreaser. Let it stand for a few minutes and hose the engine off with water. The result is as effective as steam cleaning, but isn't so tough on gaskets, wiring, and hoses. Since the degreaser removes lubrication, always oil the carb linkage, handbrake and shift linkages, manifold heat valves, and any other exposed working parts that are involved.

Clean cars usually bring a better deal at trade-in time because it's assumed that drivers who are particular about appearance are similarly careful about other forms of maintenance. One thing is certain. When your car is looking good, it's a lot easier to get inspired about doing whatever is necessary to keep it *running* good as well.

There is nothing like a summer picnic by a peaceful brook. But when the kids finally crawl back inside the car with muddy shoes and chocolate cake on their fingers, watch out!

CLEANING INTERIORS

Driving is more pleasant when your car is clean on the inside too

The cars with the worst looking interiors are those driven to work daily by factory workers. The driver's seat is usually soiled, sagging and gashed by tools left protruding from hip pockets. The drippings of countless lunch bags stain the passenger seat and carpeting. If the owner belongs to a car pool, multiply the damage by the number of riders and you have an accurate picture of the worst in car interiors.

Next in line come cars used by families

who are too lazy or too apathetic to discipline their children. Stuffing a dripping ice cream cone or a bag of french fries into the kid's face may shut him up, but by the time his muddy boots have ground the leavings into the upholstery, the cost of the high-calorie pacifier will have multiplied itself by several hundred. Once car interiors have arrived in this sad state it's usually too late to save them.

The time to attack dirt and stains is while they are still fresh. Old grime and grease eventually become an organic part of the upholstery material. If you want to own a car that's as slick on the inside as first-class accommodations on a trans-Atlantic airliner, it will take regular cleaning jobs and the immediate treatment of accidental spills or stains.

PLASTIC INTERIORS

Tough vinyls will take a scrubbing that would leave a rhinocerous raw without ill effect. Strong household detergents can be used with impunity and stubborn stains may even be rubbed away with bleach-containing scouring powder. Soft plastic interiors which more nearly resemble genuine leather should be given more restrained cleaning. Spray-foam preparations such as DuPont's "Jet Clene" are best for leather-like synthetic upholstery materials as well as for the genuine article. The cleaner consists of a "dry" foam that is applied with a sponge and rubbed dry with a soft cloth. Household detergents can be used on soft plastic interiors to get tough stains out, but never on leather.

LEATHER

Genuine leather should be washed like a baby with mild soap and water. Never use saddle soap since it leaves a grime-collecting film behind. The following procedure is recommended by The Upholstery Leather Group as well as many auto manufacturers:

Work up a dry, meringue-like lather by rubbing a cake of mild soap (such as "Ivory") with a thoroughly wrung-out pad of dampened cheesecloth. Shampoo limited areas at a time, rubbing in the direction of any pleating in the upholstery. Remove the grime-laden lather with a clean cloth and repeat if necessary. After the leather is thoroughly clean it should be buffed to a high luster using dry, clean cheesecloth.

The procedure for using DuPont "Jet Clene" or similar commercially-available products is exactly the same. Genuine leather requires no oil, wax or polish, and the application of these substances or of furniture polish, varnish, auto body wax, and other "protective" coatings will only dry out upholstery leather's natural oils

Pleated leather or vinyl materials as well as interiors done in fabric need a thorough vacuum cleaning before liquid cleaners are used. A whisk broom is OK in an emergency.

These things may be great for saddles and shoes or for giving a shine to livingroom furniture, but they are not for use on car upholstery materials, including on leather.

Foam type auto upholstery cleaners must be applied sparingly. Use a sponge for seats with smooth surfaces and a soft-bristled brush for pleated and textured materials.

Scrub small areas of upholstery at a time, making certain that pleats and seams are treated thoroughly. After the foam has absorbed the dirt it can be wiped away.

Concentrated detergents and even scouring powder can be used to scrub away stubborn stains on modern vinyl upholstery material. They are not, however, for use on leather.

Shiny painted areas inside the car can be waxed just as the outside of the car is. Do not use wax, however, on dull interior finishes. They may assume a spotty shine.

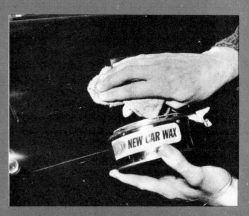

and lead to brittleness and cracking. Saddle soap, floor wax, shoe polish, or anything else needlessly smeared onto leather upholstery only provides a place for dirt to collect. The finer your car's upholstery, the more careful the cleaning must be. The use of cleaning agents such as acetone, nail polish remover, naptha, bleach, and carbon tetrachloride is both objectionable and unnecessary on leather.

FABRICS

With regular care, leather will retain a good appearance indefinitely, and plastic interiors will clean up to their original appearance even after long neglect. On the other hand, fabric interiors are as vulnerable to stains as the reputation of a Midwest schoolmarm and must be cleaned often and properly to avoid dis-

coloration. Certain common agents do a good job of coping with the more frequently encountered stains.

Grass stain can be eradicated with alcohol and/or detergent. *Lipstick* responds to ordinary undiluted household detergent. *Ballpoint ink* can be taken out with acetone, but don't try it with acetate (rayon) materials or you're likely to end up with a hole big enough to drop a polecat through. *Rust* is a "toughy," but in some cases oxalic acid can be used. This must be neutralized with ammonia after the stain is gone. It's best to try the oxalic acid on some hidden bit of the upholstery material first since it destroys some dyestuffs.

Iodine stains dissolve in fresh photographic hypo, but rinse the material thoroughly after using it. *Grease, oil, tar* and *chewing gum* can be softened and removed with drycleaning fluid, tar remover, or carbon tetrachloride. All cleaning agents should be removed with a blotter to avoid the formation of rings. Two other obnoxious stains can also be treated with some success.

Chocolate and cocoa: (1) Dampen, and let stand with liquid detergent or with a paste made from an enzyme-active detergent and water. Apply more detergent plus white vinegar. Wash clean. (2) Should a brown stain remain, sponge with hydrogen peroxide, or cover the dampened spot with powdered sodium perborate and let stand for an hour. The fabric should be tested in some out-of-sight area for color change before resorting to this step.

Blood: (1) Break up the stain if it has hardened, and test for color change before each agent is used. (2) Dampen the spot with cool water, let soak. Wash with warm enzyme-active detergent in water. (3) Sponge with a solution of one tablespoon ammonia to two quarts of water. (4) Traces of stain will respond to sponging with hydrogen peroxide containing a few drops of ammonia. (5) Rinse thoroughly!

Stains on seats, carpeting, or headliner should be removed, whenever possible, as soon as they have been made. Old stains are often impossible to remove from fabric upholstery.

Nothing beats drycleaning fluid for the

Volkswagens and a couple of other imports have batteries that are mounted under the rear seat. Keep them clean and corrosion free to prevent damage to seat, floor mat.

regular care of normally-soiled fabric interiors. Apply it sparingly so that the material is barely dampened, then wipe clean. Car interiors should always be given a thorough vacuum cleaning to remove dust and loose dirt particles before any liquid cleaning agent is applied.

CARPETS

The plain rubber floor mats found in many economy cars are easier to clean than a solid chrome cuspidor. All it takes is a good hard scrubbing with the strongest detergent you can find. Don't use cleaners or solvents containing petroleum products, however, or the rubber will get stickier than a pickpocket's finger.

Carpeting should be given a thorough vacuum cleaning and then scrubbed with household carpet cleaner. The little woman is probably an expert at this job and may be able to give you a few pointers if you can get her to lay down her movie magazine for a few minutes. Carpeting should be protected with rubber foot mats during the winter. Dripping coats and muddy overshoes will leave it hopelessly soiled if you don't. Age and sunlight may eventually cause the carpet to fade, but spray cans of auto carpet dye are available from mail-order automotive supply companies and do a good job.

Once your car is clean, keep it that way by carrying a container of spray cleaner, a sponge, and some clean cloths.

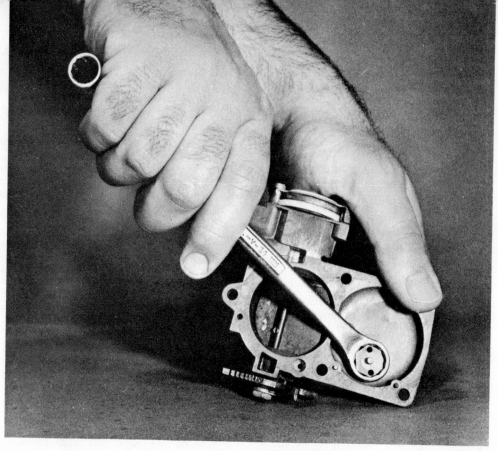

Properly fitting, high quality tools are a must if you intend to do repair work without damaging your car's parts. Metric tools should always be obtained for European made cars.

BASIC TOOLS

Having a lot of tools isn't so important as having the right ones

The day is long since past when you could tackle just about any automotive repair job with only a hammer, screwdriver, and the wrench set left over from Uncle Griswald's 1933 Hudson. Still, the number of different tools it takes to handle a majority of auto repair and maintenance operations remains surprisingly small. Today's car owner doesn't need a great many tools to keep the family transportation tuned up and in the pink, but he does need to have the *right* tools.

"Bargain" tool assortments offering a large number of pieces at a low price are not always the best way to go. There are more tricks to the tool peddling game than thirty Turkish opium smugglers could think up during an 8 to 10-year stretch on Devil's Island. Five jeweler's screwdrivers, ten identical hacksaw blades and three wood chisels may help to bolster an impressive tool count, but they are of little help to an auto mechanic. Sets featuring an impressive socket wrench set can also be a poor choice since there are many other tools needed for working on cars and about half the socket sizes in a full set can be used only once in a fuscia moon for automotive repairs.

BASIC LIST

Tools For Threaded Fasteners

1. *Socket wrench set* with breaker bar, ratchet handle, and 7/16, 1/2, 9/16, 5/8, 11/16 and 3/4-inch socket sizes. (9, 10, 12, 13, 14, 15, 17, 19, and 22-millimeter sizes for European cars.)
2. Box end/open-end combination wrench set in the same size as listed above, (Due to the larger number of sizes, European car owners may have to select separate box-end and open-end wrench sets rather than combination wrenches.)
3. *Small 1/4" drive socket set* for fastener sizes from 3/16" to 3/8". (6, 7, 8, 9, and 10-millimeter for cars with metric fasteners.)
4. *Small combination wrench set* covering the same range as the above. (Foreign car owners may find that these sizes are included as a part of

sets that also handle larger size fasteners.)
5. *An adjustable wrench* with a capacity of 1 1/4".
6. Five screwdrivers ranging from small to very large in size.
7. Three Phillips screwdrivers in sizes #1, #2, and #3.
8. *A set of Allen setscrew wrenches.*
9. *A spark plug socket,* plus individual sockets and extensions needed for special jobs on your particular car.

Other Hand Tools

1. *Medium weight ball-peen hammer.*
2. *8-inch lineman's pliers.*
3. *Channellock adjustable pliers.*
4. *Long-nose pliers.*
5. *Cold chisel, center punch, drift driver set.*

CHOOSING TOOLS

The above list should be considered the minimum necessary for common automotive maintenance jobs. The sockets and box-end wrenches should be of the 12-point variety which will fit the occasional square bolt or nut in addition to the predominating hex type. Most engines

This socket wrench set below, contains a complete range of useful sizes. There are 1/2", 3/8" and 1/4" drive sizes included, a range from 3/16" to 1 1/8" bolts. These tools are a must.

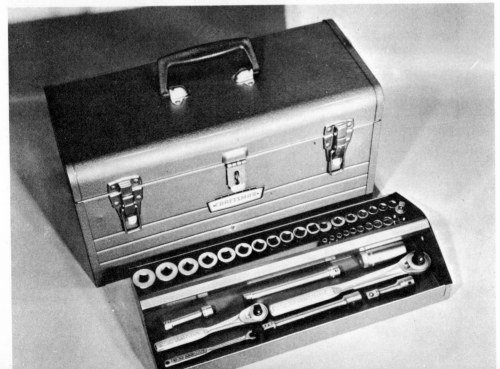

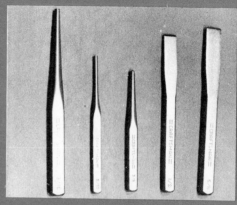

Big machinery requires bigger wrenches. The ¾″ drive socket on the left is the kind needed for big trucks. Others are largest sockets in ½, ⅜ and ¼ drives.

Cold chisels for cutting corroded bolts or splitting rusty mufflers should be in your tool kit along with punches for driving drift pins or locating holes to be drilled.

require a 13/16″ spark plug socket, but certain late GM cars employ the ⅝″ size. Individual sockets, such as a 1 1/16″ size to fit most front wheel bearings or a 1 7/16-incher to remove VW rear axle nuts may be obtained as needed rather than purchasing an all-inclusive socket set that contains these sizes. Mercedes-Benz, as well as several other European manufacturers, make use of bolts having a hex hollow in their heads similar to those found in Allen setscrews. A special metric accessory set is available from the better tool companies for these fittings.

The more elaborate "professional" socket wrench sets include sizes such as 15/32″, 17/32″, 19/32″, and 13/16″. These fall in between the more common socket sizes. While not frequently used, fasteners of these dimensions are occasionally encountered in special assemblies such as air conditioner compressors and other places where the car maker would just as soon discourage casual tinkering. Regardless of what kind of wrench set you buy, take along a few representative nuts and bolts and try them on for size. Cheap wrenches will chew the corners off bolt heads quicker than a hungry termite can go through a grain of sawdust. Tools that don't fit accurately are no bargain at any price.

Deep or long reach sockets are needed for many specific jobs, particularly in the case of engine rebuilding. A set such as this can be had for under $20 to augment your main set.

Hex keys for Allen type setscrews come in a wide range of sizes. You should have a set like this for common work and a metric selection for cars such as Mercedes Benz.

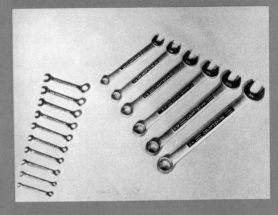

Open-end/box-end combination wrenches are the handiest type for general repair work. Two sets—such as those shown—are able to handle all sizes from 3/16″ to 3/4″.

DRIVE SIZE

Sockets having ⅜″ square drives are adequate for the bulk of all automotive work, but because socket sizes greater than 1-inch are often not available in anything other than ½″ drive, this drive size is by far the most popular. However, ⅜″ drive socket sets are more compact and and can reach into places that might prevent the use of ½″ drive tools. Many professional mechanics therefore prefer a set of ⅜″ drive tools for small engines, motorcycles, and automobiles, plus a basic group of ¾″ drive tools for heavier automotive jobs as well as for trucks and tractors.

SCREWDRIVERS

The best screwdrivers are not necessarily the most expensive. When your hands are greasier than a giggolo's pompadore, square wooden handles are far easier to grip than plastic. A blade of high-quality square tool steel stock is also more rigid than a round shank. The portion of the blade which engages the screw slot should have its widest part in line with the flat sides of the square shank and not with one of its corners—it's stronger that way. Auto supply stores regularly sell such screwdrivers in low-priced sets.

While they don't look very fancy, they're about the best tool ever devised for removing and installing screws.

PLIERS

Common slip-joint pliers have a large following among "filling station" mechanics. Their use, however, accounts for more wrecked fuel line fittings, water jacket drain taps, and assorted fasteners than anyone would ever care to admit. Lineman's pliers are a better bet. They double as wirecutters and can handle everything from snipping off cotter pins to twisting bailing wire with admirable ease.

If you have something large to grip, Channellock pliers are preferable to the ordinary slip-joint type. Don't settle for the off-brand imitators that are often sold under the generic name "channel lock." The genuine Channellock brand is unsurpassed for gripping work firmly and evenly and will prevent a great many wrecked parts and bruised knuckles.

If the home mechanic will take the time to select his tool carefully and to obtain the items included on this basic list he should be able to handle any maintenance or repair operation that his car demands. Certain cars may require a few special tools, but for the run-of the highway go-buggy, the basics are enough.

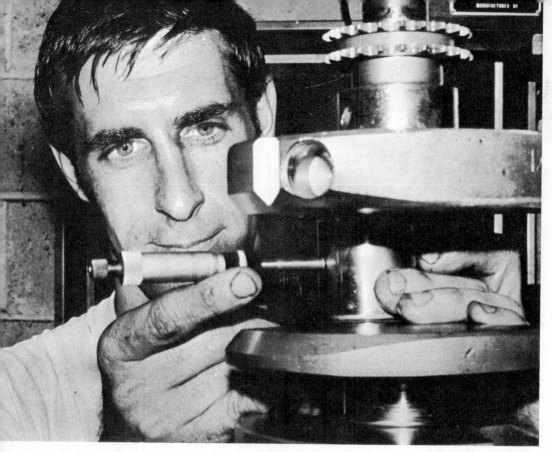

Top racing engine builder Paul Cole mikes crankshaft journal in at least six places before he decides whether it's ready for competition. Such work really requires precision.

MEASURING TOOLS

It's not hard to do precision work when you have the proper tools

You don't have to be a professional machinist to appreciate precision measuring tools. One item that belongs in every car owner's tool kit is an ordinary round-wire spark plug gauge. This little gadget alone can save a motorist from enduring countless run-down batteries, expensive tows, and emergency road service calls. Spark plug gaps that have become excessively wide due to long service are the cause of most cold-weather no-starts. A periodic re-gapping will do it.

FEELER GAUGES

Flat feeler gauges have fewer applications than formerly due to the wide use of hydraulic valve lifters. Dwell meters have largely replaced them for adjusting distributor points as well. Nevertheless, most imported cars, domestic sub-compacts, and economy models still permit feeler gauge adjustments. As you've probably guessed, a bushel of feeler gauges sells for less than one dwell meter.

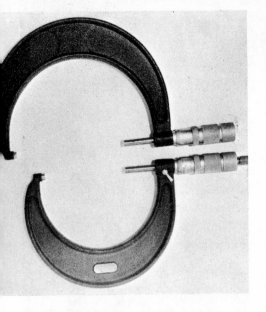

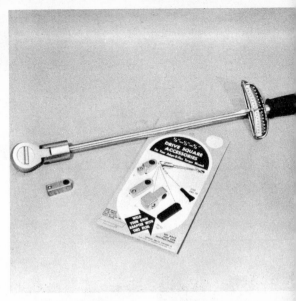

Micrometers come in different sizes for different jobs. Big job is for miking 4" to 5" pistons. Lower micrometer can be locked at any particular setting by lever.

A precision measuring tool which every car owner should have is shown here. This new "Adapt-O-Flex" torque wrench can be used with ratchet, or any sizes of square drive.

MICROMETERS

Micrometers are almost a "must" for engine rebuilds and overhauls. Although it's possible to fit new bearings, pistons, and piston rings without a "mike," there's always a chance that irregular crankshaft wear or variations in piston fit will go unnoticed and cause trouble once the engine has been returned to service. Sears markets a micrometer set with interchangeable anvils to handle diameters from 0 to 4 inches for less than $50. This is about the best deal possible. A set of telescoping rod gauges will allow micrometer to measure inside diameters.

TORQUE WRENCHES

Every grade of bolt has a limit to which it can be tightened before it starts to stretch and lose strength. Expensive parts may be distorted or cracked by over-tightening bolts, and under-torqued fasteners are often subjected to fluctuating loads which will eventually cause them to fail. These are conditions that only a

torque wrench can prevent.

Torque, or twisting force, is commonly measured in foot-pounds. Five foot-pounds of torque are applied to a fastener when five pounds of pressure are exerted at the end of a foot-long wrench. Motorcycles and small engines sometimes have their torque specifications given in inch-pounds, or 1/12 of a foot-pound. Although European torque specifications are given in meter-kilograms (mkg), manuals printed in English usually substitute the foot-pound equivalent. Nevertheless, torque wrenches are available which include the metric figures in addition to the normal foot-pound or inch-pound scales.

Whenever possible, torque wrenches should be used within the middle two-quarters of their range. A 100 foot-pound capacity wrench is therefore best suited to gauging torques between 25 and 75 foot-pounds. This size is considered best for most automotive work, but professional mechanics often choose a pair of torque wrenches, one reading to 50 foot-pounds and the other to 150.

A vernier caliper can be useful for many measuring tasks, but despite the fact that they measure to 1/1,000 inch, most of the auto mechanics prefer to use micrometers alone.

A full family of micrometers to cover the full 0 to five-inch range is a very costly proposition. However, Sears offers a good combination set at considerably lower cost.

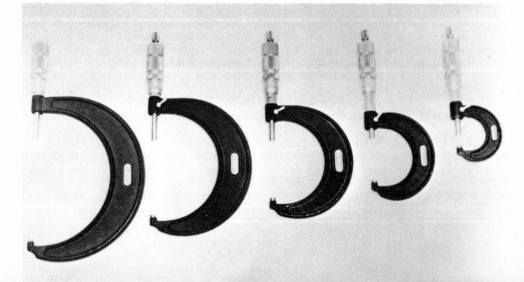

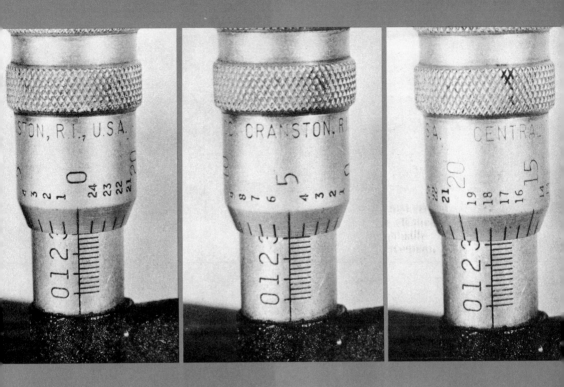

Scale on stationary sleeve of micrometer reads tenths of an inch. With thimble at "zero" this micrometer is positioned as it would be when measuring an exact 3/10". If the micrometer's thimble (center) is rotated to 5 past its zero a difference of 5/1,000 inch is indicated. The total reading on the micrometer scale is now .305-inch. Advancing the thimble further (at right) .018" shows on the rotating scale. The total reading is now .318-inch. The total range of any micrometer, in fact, is one inch or 40 rotations.

The range of any torque wrench can be increased through the use of adapters. These are not available as ready-made tools, but directions for making your own are given in the instruction booklets supplied with the torque wrench. An adapter that is half as long as the torque wrench itself will increase its capacity by ½ times. A 100 foot-pound wrench can therefore be made to work up to 150 foot-pounds with a half-length extension and up to 200 foot-pounds with a full length adapter.

There are many types of torque wrenches being manufactured, but the flexible-beam variety is the least expensive and most practical for the home me-chanic. They have no delicate moving parts and will take rougher use and re-main accurate over longer periods of time than the mechanical kind will.

Although not included in the basic list of hand tools, a torque wrench is virtually indispensable for servicing modern auto-mobiles. This is especially true of engines that make extensive use of light alloy castings. Plug gauges and feeler gauges are rather basic too, at least for car own-ers who intend to do their own tune-ups. Micrometers and vernier calipers can wait until you decide to try your hand at an engine overhaul, but feeler gauges and a good torque wrench should probably be on hand from the very start.

A cooling system pressure tester can spot leaks and determine overheating troubles almost instantly, but it is not the sort of tool needed outside a busy service station.

TEST INSTRUMENTS

Before you can repair your car, you have to find out what's wrong

Let's assume that your car's engine runs rough and stalls whenever it is left idling. There are at least four things which could be causing the trouble. The expensive way to pinpoint the cause would be to replace all parts which might be faulty. The quickest and cheapest way, however, is to buy a few test instruments so that you can locate such malfunctions without resorting to "cut and try" methods.

Inexpensive tune-up sets that include a compression gauge, vacuum gauge/fuel pump tester, and a timing light are perfectly adequate for home use. The items on the following list can be purchased for well under thirty dollars and will pay for themselves the first time they tell you that your stalling problem is caused by a leaking carburetor flange gasket and you haven't had to hire a mechanic to find it out.

BASIC LIST

1. Compression gauge
2. Vacuum gauge
3. Timing Light
4. Dwell meter/tachometer
5. Battery hydrometer
6. Radiator hydrometer
7. Test Light
8. Tire pressure gauge
9. Spark plug tester

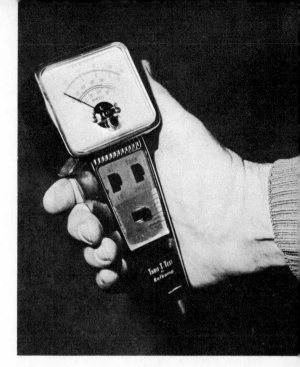

A dwell meter for checking and adjusting distributor points is perhaps the most complex test instrument needed by the home mechanic for routine maintenance work.

A simple tire pressure gauge is within the financial reach of every car owner and can easily be worth many times its cost both in terms of safety and in added tire life.

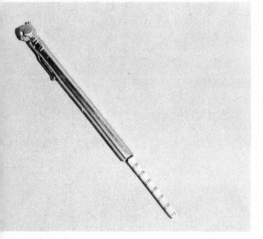

Vacuum gauges are a highly accurate means of determining the condition of an engine and a great aid to carb adjustments. Some car owners mount them on the dash.

Whether or not you need a $10 to $20 dwell meter depends largely on the kind of car you drive. Although most small domestic cars and all imports can have their distributor points set using an ordinary feeler gauge, most big American V-8's have their distributors in such inaccessible locations that precise settings are hardly possible without the use of a dwell meter.

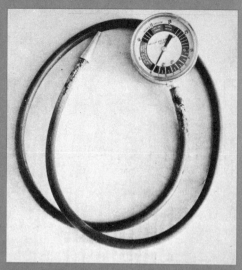

A vacuum gauge is probably the most useful test instrument for doing tune-ups. It's a "must" for adjusting carburetors on most all cars with exhaust emission controls.

Power timing lights, such as this, cost more than simple neon tube type, but they put out a much stronger light so that it is not necessary to work in a darkened garage.

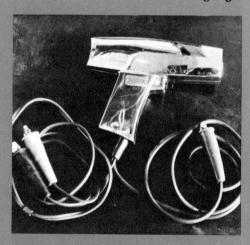

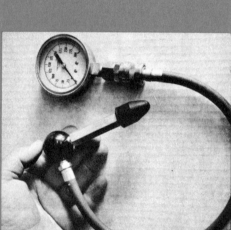

Compression gauges which will accept a flexible hose and interchangeable fittings are needed to take cylinder pressure readings on many of the large V-eight engines.

An ignition tester will tell instantly if the coil is weak or if the ignition system is generally not up to par. However, it's only for troubleshooting, not for general tune-up.

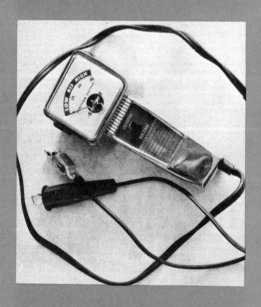

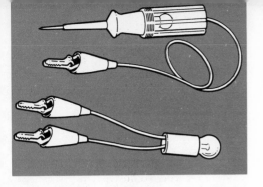

Test lights are valuable for tracking down electrical troubles. Top type has a small battery which allows it to operate independently of the car's electrical system.

A compression gauge such as this can be inserted into the spark plug holes of each cylinder. Low readings indicate the need for a valve grinding or piston ring work.

Hydrometers are another inexpensive test device. They are used to check battery charge levels (RIGHT) or to test out the anti-freeze content of the radiator (LEFT).

If you are handy with your hands there are several test tools you can make at home. The flashlight was converted to test light, the test condenser made from ignition part.

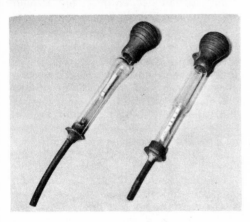

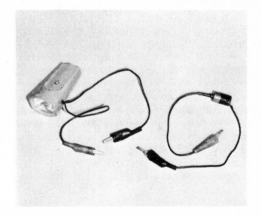

Test lights are extremely useful, and car owners can easily make their own at very low cost. Two test leads soldered onto an ordinary automobile light bulb will enable you to determine if electrical current is reaching a particular light or accessory when the switch is turned on. A test light that has its own batteries has wide use for testing alternator, generator, starter, and electric motor components. A neon type spark plug and cable tester costs about $1.80 and will tell you whether or not individual spark plugs are firing.

Regular checks with a compression gauge can detect an engine that is ready for a valve job. It's always better to perform such repairs at your leisure than to suddenly find yourself with a sick car half-way across the Rockies during your summer vacation. The tire gauge is important too. A quick check at home will let you know if you should head for the turnpike or for the corner tire shop.

It might be argued that merely *buying* the test instruments listed here will not automatically provide the know-how required to use them. The instructions furnished by their manufacturers help. But keep reading, such details are covered fully later in the book.

SPECIAL TOOLS

These tools aren't needed often,

but they can still be lifesavers

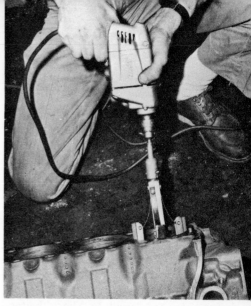

Special tools such as a cylinder hone, a cylinder ridge reamer and a valve spring compressor are needed for engine rebuilds and valve grind work. Buy as need arises.

Jack stands, wheel ramps, and chain hoists are tools that can be lifesavers in a very literal sense. The ordinary bumper jacks supplied with American cars are hardly safe for changing tires, let alone for supporting a car while someone is working under it. Wheel ramps allow the car to be driven onto them, but jack stands are often more practical since the wheels can be removed from the car while it is supported off the ground. A chain hoist is especially useful for lifting out ailing engines. Finding a place to hang it can be a problem, however.

A work bench and bench vise are indispensable for certain "heavy" automotive repairs. Fortunately, most home workshop enthusiasts are likely to have such equipment already. Some cars need special tools to handle particular jobs. General Motors distributors require a unique hollow screwdriver to remove the ignition points. Curved wrenches are needed to remove exhaust manifold bolts on several American V-8 engines. Special tool sets are also a "must" for working on automatic transmissions. The Proto Tool Company markets such an assortment, including a booklet listing detailed instructions for automatic transmissions.

A propane torch may be required for heating corroded, frozen parts so that they can be separated. A power drill with a variable speed control is also a highly versatile tool. In addition to drilling holes, hand drills can be used with a sanding disc for body repair, a wire bush for cleaning cylinder heads and other parts, or with an abrasive stone to grind off rust-locked bolts or polish cylinder head ports. If you own a power drill you should also have a set of bolt extractors for removing broken fasteners from threaded parts.

Tin shears, soldering irons, various types of files and other tools used for fabrication and cutting may likewise be called for from time to time. A hacksaw is particularly useful. Choose one with a rigid frame that doesn't flex during use. High-speed blades, which are the sharpest and longest-lasting type, are rather brittle and can be easily broken if the frame allows them to twist or bend. Use fine-toothed blades, 32 teeth to the inch, which are generally best suited to cutting hard materials and tubing. The new round blades coated with rough tungsten carbide are excellent tools and can cut in any direction without stopping to change the position of the blade. There is nothing better for cutting old exhaust pipes, etc.

If you have a work bench, you should also consider buying a bench grinder. It will handle chisel sharpening and other grinding jobs that are too big for your power drill. With the addition of a buffing wheel you can use it to give a mirror finish to aluminum parts. Add a wire brush and it's also great for cleaning up valves before grinding them and for removing rust from old parts being refurbished.

A valve spring compressor, cylinder hone, cylinder ridge reamer, and piston

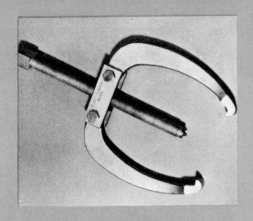

A gear puller is needed for many repair operations and not always for pulling off gears. With attachments they'll remove wheel bearings and withdraw rear axles.

A bench grinder can be one of the most worthwhile tools a car owner can have in his garage. Wire bush is particularly useful for cleaning up rusty, dirty parts.

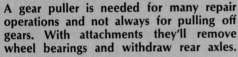

Ingenuity can make special tools from many common tools. A length of wire chain has been used to convert this ordinary wheel puller into a tool for pulling brake drums.

An electric drill having built-in speed control is best for starting holes and for operating such tools as cylinder hones and wire brushes. Well worth extra cost.

ring compressor are special tools needed for engine overhauls. These are fairly expensive items and may not pay for themselves until you've done two or three engine jobs. Wheel pullers, needed to remove brake drums on some cars, and a slide hammer for pulling axles may also be rather expensive if you only intend to use them for one job. A brake cylinder hone may be worth purchasing for a single repair, but some of the other special tools mentioned here should be looked for at a tool rental company before you resort to buying your own. Tool rental

shops may also have such highly specialized automotive repair equipment such as valve grinding machines and cylinder boring mills. Such rental services can be "moneysavers" as well as "lifesavers" for home mechanics faced with major jobs.

Tools are something that most car owners accumulate rather gradually, or as needed. But don't neglect obtaining some of the more important "special" tools right from the start. A pair of jack stands or wheel ramps could keep you from being "depressed" while doing your very first home lube job. Think about it.

If your car looks this way after the wreck it's probably too big a job to tackle at home. However, touching up damaged paint and fixing small dents isn't hard work at all.

PAINT AND BODY WORK

Here's how to fix chipped paint and erase minor scrapes and dents

Stone chips and scratched paint caused by a multitude of daily hazards are usually the first thing to take the "new" off new cars. Minor nicks are best filled with touch-up paint rather than resorting to any extensive refinishing. Suitable containers of touch-up paint can be obtained from your car dealer complete with a "fingernail polish" brush for applying it. Actually, such brushes are too big for most paint chips. A very small, pointed artist's water color brush does a much better job.

"Fingernail polish" repairs are not acceptable for correcting anything larger than the tiniest chips or scratches. The spray cans of touch-up paint sold in most auto supply and discount stores are far superior for repainting damaged areas ranging from the size of a pencil eraser to about a foot in diameter. You'll also need a couple sheets of #220-grit paper to remove loose rust and brighten the underlying metal. Another two sheets of #320-grit paper will be required for feathering the paint surrounding the dam-

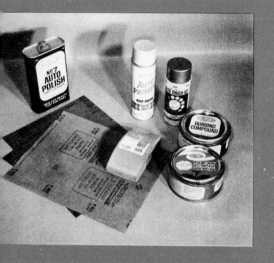

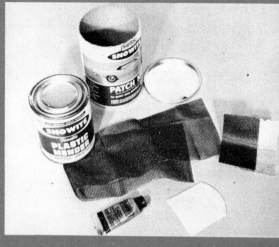

Here's what you need for paint touch-ups. Three or four grades of sandpaper, rubber sanding block, primer, touch-up paint, a can of rubbing compound, polish and wax.

Body mending kits such as this have both plastic body filler for hiding dents and fiberglass for glassing in rust holes and tears. It's an easy job even for beginners.

aged area. One sheet each of #360, #380, and #400-grit paper should be on hand for bringing the primer to mirror smoothness, and a sheet of #600-grit will will be needed if wet-sanding the finish coat proves necessary. Naturally you'll also have to have a spray can of auto body primer and possibly a rubber sanding block for attacking larger jobs.

PREPARATION

Unless the area being repaired is given proper preparation, the finished job will be about as attractive as a shrunken head mixed into a plate of meatballs. Remove all dirt and old wax with a strong detergent. Sand away loose paint and rust until nothing remains except bright metal surrounded by sound paint. Featheredge the paint around the damaged spot with dry #320-grit paper. Keep hacking away until broad concentric rings of primer and finish can be seen all around the bare spot. Always sand in one direction, never with a circular motion.

PRIMING

Wipe away all dust and sanding residue, then mask off surrounding areas with masking tape and newspaper. For masking very small areas, merely cut a hole through a fairly large sheet of cardboard and hold this about an inch away from the car so that the spray will reach the area being repaired only where it passes through the hole.

When spraying, depress the button while the nozzle is aimed off to one side of the touch-up area. Any spatters caused by the opening of the spray valve will then fall onto the masking paper and not the car. Hold the can 12 to 15 inches away from the work and move the spray across the prepared area smoothly keeping the button fully depressed. Wait until the spray is once again directed against the masking paper before releasing the valve.

Let the primer dry for five to ten minutes between coats. Three coats will usually be enough, but primer should be ap-

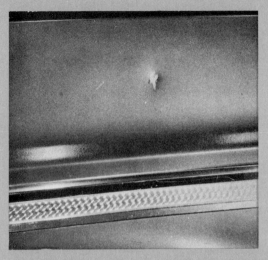

Have you ever come back to your car after leaving it in a parking lot and found one of these ugly dings in the fender or door? Here's how to fix it one step at a time:

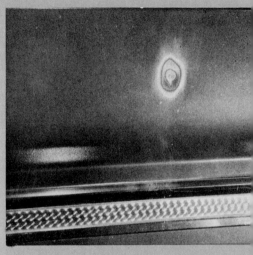

Sand away damaged paints, feathering the area out into the surrounding finish. The depression can be hammered out somewhat, but not completely without bulging metal.

plied in successive thin layers until the repaired area is built up almost to the level of the surrounding paint. Let the primer dry for half an hour after the last coat before sanding it.

SANDING THE PRIMER

Color coats usually hide less of what's underneath them than a burlesque queen's see-through nighty. The final finish therefore depends on how well you wet-sand the primer coat. A trickle from a garden hose or a sponge should be allowed to run evenly over the area being sanded. Keep the body wet so that the sandpaper floats over the primer without dragging or digging in. Sand in one direction without pressure using smooth steady motions.

Remove any rough areas with #360-grit paper. Use #380-grit to smooth the primer and blend it into the surrounding paint. Finish the job with #400-grit paper and plenty of water and you should end up with a surface that's smoother

than an undertaker presenting an overdue bill. Let the primer dry for another 24 hours before painting over it.

SPRAYING THE COLOR

Once again mask surrounding areas of the body or get out your cardboard sheet with the hole in it. Shake the can of color coat thoroughly and start spraying off to one side of the touch-up area just as you did when applying the primer. Depress the button fully to avoid incompletely atomized paint and keep the nozzle at least one foot from the work to avoid air bubbles in the finish. Never stop the motion of the spray or change directions while it is directed against the work area.

It cannot be emphasized too strongly that *each coat should be very thin*. Do not attempt to cover the repaired area with color on the first coat. You'll probably will be able to see the color of the primer even after the third coat if you are spraying lightly enough. The first coat of lac-

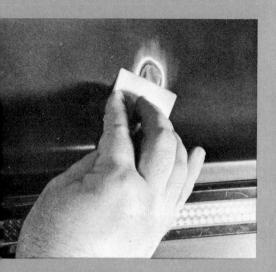

The remaining dent can be sanded to bare metal and filled with plastic mender. A small, deep dent is almost impossible to shrink completely flat by hammering alone.

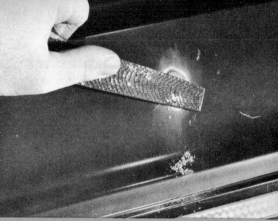

Excess body filler can be removed with a rasp, body file or coarse sandpaper. Both flexible and hard-setting fillers are sold and the latter are best for work like this.

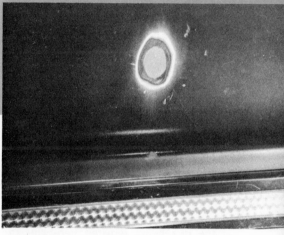

Finish filled and patched areas using a rubber sanding block. This will help make the patch even and exactly flush with the surface of the body metal surrounding it.

Mask trim and featheredge the paint around the damaged area so that broad bands of primer and color coats are visible. Note that sanding has removed other tiny chips.

quer will be ready to spray over in five minutes, as will the second. Wait ten minutes before applying a fourth coat and 15 to 20 minutes before spraying a fifth.

RUBBING OUT

The color coat should dry at least 24 hours before it is rubbed out. Dust flecks, bubbles, and sags can be sanded out using #600-grit paper, lots of water, and very light sanding. Enamels, however, must never be sanded.

The color coat will require rubbing out to obtain a high gloss—especially if sanding was necessary. Apply the rubbing compound with a soft cloth pad and work in spirals starting at the edges of the repaired area. When the spot has been blended into the car's original finish, work inward until the repaired area has a high luster. Rub lightly and avoid localized pressure. Do as little rub-out work as you can to avoid going through the color coat. Follow the rub-out with a body wax that contains fine abrasive cleaners.

DENTED METAL

Minor body damage frequently accompanies chipped paint. If the dent is small and difficult to reach from behind, sand it down to bare metal and fill the depression with plastic body filler. The filler is sanded smooth after it dries and the repaired area prepared, primed, and painted as described earlier.

Larger dents should be pounded out as much as possible before resorting to filler. A basic set of body repair tools can be obtained for about five dollars which will be adequate for this purpose. Dents stretch the metal, and if you merely hammer them from the back you'll end up with an outward bulge in the panel rather than a smooth surface. Start by striking the center of the dent from behind with a hand dolly. This will cause the metal to bulge outward around the edge of the dent. Hold the dolly against the back of the dent's center while pounding down the bulge surrounding the outer edge of the dent with a hammer. Keep working in toward the center, raising a bulge then hammering it out, until dent is smoothed.

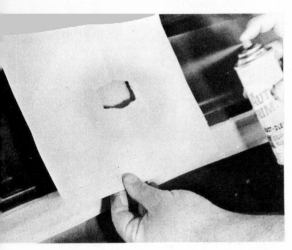

When spraying primer onto small areas such as the one being repaired here you can use a sheet of paper with a central hole to mask the car's finish from the overspray.

After the primer has dried it must be wet sanded to a glass-smooth finish. Slowly wring out a sponge over work, don't press, and finish up with #400-grit sandpaper.

Spraying the primer is the most important part of touch-up work. Continue applying coats until surface is built up to that of the car's original finish. Use thin coats.

After the primer has been sanded it should blend smoothly into the surrounding finish. The color coat around the spot should also be lightly sanded to obtain the best job.

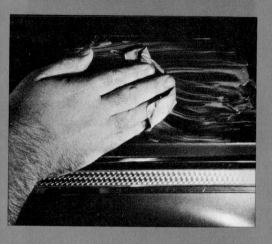

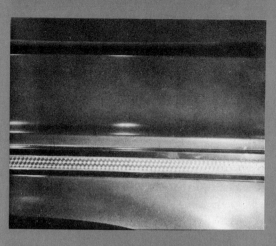

Spray the color coat as described in the text, allowing it to mist out onto the surrounding paint lightly. After it's dry use rubbing compound, polish, and then wax.

The finished job is so perfect that it is impossible to tell where the repair was made. This is certainly prettier than any dent, paint chip, or rust stain ever was!

FINISHING

Once the damaged area has been straightened as much as possible, it should be worked with a rubber sanding block and #200-grit paper. This will cause the high spots to show up as bright metal and leave low spots covered by paint. Continued light hammer and dolly work will correct these minor irregularities. Low spots that can't be brought up without bulging the surrounding metal may be hidden with body filler when necessary. Once the area sands smooth, you can featheredge the surrounding paint and refinish in the regular way.

RUST DAMAGE

There's no cure for rust, but you can patch up the after effects to keep older cars looking better longer. Fiberglass patching kits are easy enough for anybody to use. These consist of a few pieces of fiberglass cloth, resin and hardener. Plastic body filler can also be used to fill small rust holes. Persistent rusting usually occurs when the metal is somewhat porous. The closest thing to a cure is sealing it from the back. Undercoating helps, and a spray can of the stuff can be used to patch up spots where the original job has chipped off.

If rust occurs at the bottoms of doors or along the lower body, take off the door liners or side upholstery, wire brush the loose rust away, and spray several coats of Rust-oleum damp-proof red primer over the areas after the rust damage has been repaired with filler or fiberglass. This will usually prevent a recurrence of the problem. Instructions furnished with body patching kits give full details for their use.

Commercial "Quickie" touch-up and putty jobs often start rusting and flaking in less than six months. Do your own touch-up work taking time for proper preparation and careful finishing and you'll be sure it's permanent—which is something you can't say about the job you'll get from 'ol "Blow-Gun Earl," the community collision corrector. Build your confidence with small touch ups, and someday you might even become brave enough to repaint your own car!

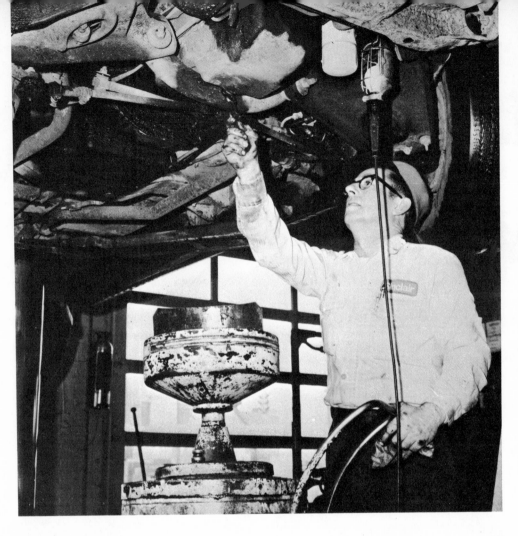

When you're able to find reliable service for your car you should consider yourself lucky. Countless drivers have decided to save money and do routine service at home.

LUBE IT YOURSELF

Oil changes and lube jobs are the tyro mechanic's training ground

Even car owners who never get closer to a screwdriver than a barstool at the corner gin mill can learn to do an oil change with less trouble than it takes to read one of Howard Johnson's menus. If you've decided that home auto maintenance is for you, but have had less experience with cars than George Washing-ton's butler, doing your own routine lubrication jobs is one of the best possible ways to become familiar with your car and to develop confidence in coping with mechanical operations. What's more, the pay is excellent.

The gas pump jocky at your neighborhood filling station isn't asking to check

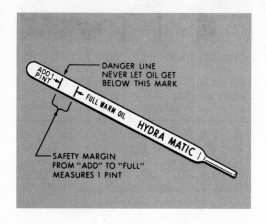

DANGER LINE
NEVER LET OIL GET
BELOW THIS MARK

SAFETY MARGIN
FROM "ADD" TO "FULL"
MEASURES 1 PINT

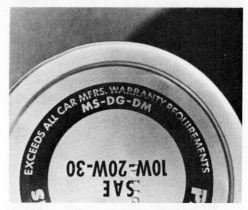

Learn to use the dipsticks on your car and know what the readings mean. Automatics have "fill" and "full" lines that are a pint apart, engines are marked in quarts.

Read the small print on motor oil cans, not the grand-sounding trade names. The A.P.I. service rating is the only true indication of whether oil suits your car.

the oil just to be helpful. He stands to make a very handsome profit every time a quart goes into some customer's engine. Top-quality oils that retail for 85¢ in most service stations can be found at prices 15¢ to 35¢ cheaper in discount stores. Even if the town grease slinger doesn't tack on a service charge for pouring the stuff into your crankcase you can still "earn" $1 or $2 every time you change oil at home.

DIPSTICK CHECKS

If the oil level in your engine's crankcase gets too low the machinery could start making some very expensive noises. On the other hand, over-filling not only wastes oil like a drunken barber but can damage oil seals, cause lost power and produce poor running. Pull the dipstick every couple of days (your owner's manual will tell you where it is), wipe it off, and stick it back into the engine. The motor should not be running. Pull it out again and note how far the oil comes up on its lower end. If the dipstick is wet up to the line marked "FULL," you do not need to add oil. Should the oil level only reach the line marked "FILL," it's safe to add a quart without overfilling the crankcase. Fastidious car owners may

prefer to add a fraction of a quart periodically to keep the oil at the "Full" line, but it's considered "safe" to operate the car normally so long as the level falls between the "FULL" and "FILL" lines.

Automatic transmissions have a dipstick too. The engine should be warmed up and idling with the selector in "P" (Park) while the fluid level is being checked. There's only a pint difference between the "FULL" and "FILL" marks on the transmission dipstick. Level is critical and must be kept in the "SAFE" zone between the two marks at all times. Never over-fill, and don't add any fluid until the fluid is down to the "ADD ONE PINT" line.

THE OIL TO ADD

Every car made in the past ten years, whether domestic or imported, requires detergent oil. All cars currently manufactured require oils with an American Petroleum Institute rating of "MS." Until 1971 there were three API ratings of interest to car owners. These were ML (light service), MM (moderate service) and MS (severe service).

ML oils are unsuitable for any modern car. MM oils, particularly special Pennsylvania-crude non-detergent types, are

Most recent cars do not have provision for draining the rear axle, but there's a plug for checking the level and filling it. A trickle of oil should come out when full.

Manual transmissions are checked as rear axles are and filled if necessary. Most automatics have no drain plug, however pan must be removed to drain old fluid.

Various types of hand grease guns are sold for home use. This car has had grease fittings installed in place of plugs to make regular home servicing possible.

still favorites for certain vintage sports cars. For your car and mine, an MS oil is the only thing that will do.

In 1970 the API revised its service designations and in 1971 the labeling on cans began to change accordingly. Under the new system ML was changed to SA (spark ignition class "A"). MM is now SB and SC is used to designate oils which meet the MS standards laid down in 1964. SD will be used to designate oils that conform to the MS standards that went into effect in 1968. Prior to this change, car owners had to look for words to the effect that the oil "exceeds new-car warranty requirements" to know whether the lubricant met the latest MS standards. The SC rating will also make the listing of such auto maker's standards as GM 6042-M or Ford M2C 101-B unnecessary since the SD rating assures the buyer that these standards are met by the product. Your car owner's manual will list the standards established for your particular automobile.

Most oil containers bear several other designations in addition to the one of primary interest to the average car owner. Among these are diesel ratings. The old system consisted of DG (diesel general service), DM (diesel moderate service), and DS (diesel severe service). The new API service designations substitute CA (compression ignition class "A") for DG, CB and CC for the lower and upper range of the group formerly called DM, and uses CD in place of the former DS rating.

Automatic transmission fluid meeting current auto manufacturer's standards is

marked AQ-ATF, Suffix A (or Type A). If it's not, all the grand trade names in the world are not going to make it suitable for use in your car.

VISCOSITY

Designations such as "S.A.E. 10W" describe an oil's *viscosity index* and have nothing to with "weight." All oil has a specific gravity of less than 1.00, and even molasses-thick gear oils will float on water. Viscosity is a term used to indicate *how easily a liquid flows*. Although water has greater weight than an S.A.E. 40 motor oil, it flows more easily. The oil, however, has higher viscosity. The "W" in S.A.E. 10W does not mean "weight" but *winter*, and indicates that the oil achieves a S.A.E. (Society of Automotive Engineers) flow rate of 10 at 0° F. rather than at the 210° figure used in measuring "summer" oils.

Nearly all car makers now recommend multi-viscosity oils. This is partially dictated by today's longer oil change intervals since an oil put into the engine in January may still be there in June. In the past, higher-viscosity straight grades were used in summer and S.A.E. 20W, 10W or 5W put in during the colder months.

Multi-grade oils are greatly superior to straight grades as cold weather oils. You can depend on them never to thin out on long high speed trips during the midwinter holidays. Don't try to second-guess the auto manufacturer when it comes to oil viscosity. Stick to the recommendations given in the owner's manual and forget the rumors and old wives tales you might have heard.

SERVICE INTERVALS

Car makers have been extending oil change and other lubrication intervals lately. This is merely a selling point and does nothing at all to extend the life of your car. Six-thousand mile or six-month oil changes have become almost universal but not retroactive to older cars. It's interesting to note, however, that surveys taken among various auto enthusiast groups show that car buffs distrust the long change interval recommendations

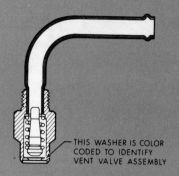

THIS WASHER IS COLOR CODED TO IDENTIFY VENT VALVE ASSEMBLY

Nearly all auto makers now require that the PCV valve be cleaned at each lube job and replaced annually. It's vital to get the correct replacement, so check specs.

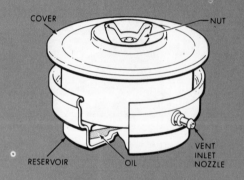

COVER — NUT
VENT INLET NOZZLE
RESERVOIR — OIL

Some cars, particularly those designed for service in dusty areas, are equipped with oil bath air cleaners. They require new oil and cleaning at each lube interval.

One of the most vital lubrication areas is the manifold heat riser valve. Not all cars have it. If your car does, obtain a special solvent/lubricant for the purpose.

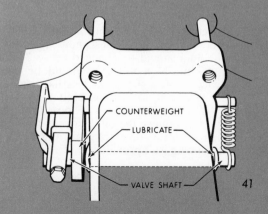

COUNTERWEIGHT
LUBRICATE
VALVE SHAFT

41

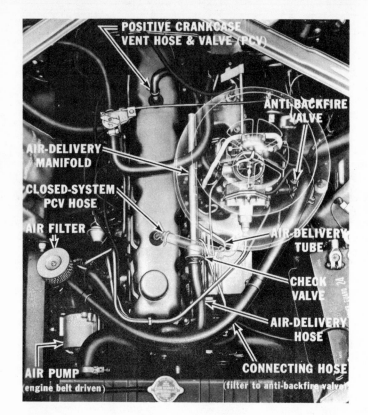

POSITIVE CRANKCASE VENT HOSE & VALVE (PCV)

ANTI-BACKFIRE VALVE

AIR-DELIVERY MANIFOLD

CLOSED-SYSTEM PCV HOSE

AIR FILTER

AIR-DELIVERY TUBE

CHECK VALVE

AIR-DELIVERY HOSE

AIR PUMP (engine belt driven)

CONNECTING HOSE (filter to anti-backfire valve)

Another part of routine servicing is a thorough check of emission controls. Air filters need charging and hoses and valves should be checked for cracks and dirt.

Photo Courtesy
American Motors Corporation

given for modern cars and seldom keep the same oil in their engines past the 3,000 mile mark. Some car owners stick to the 4,000 miles or 60 days recommendation which was current a few years ago, while others insist that you should change oil any time it becomes necessary to add a third quart between changes. Following the manufacturer's specifications is OK *if you use the quality of oil recommended*, but most conscientious motorists choose to act on the premise that oil is cheaper than new parts and therefore change more often.

Although automatic transmission manufacturers used to say that fluid changes were unnecessary, most now agree that the fluid should be changed every 24,000 miles or 24 months. It should be done twice as often if the car gets hard service in mountain areas or is used for towing purposes. It's necessary to loosen the pan bolts or remove the oil filler pipe from the pan to drain some transmissions since a drain plug isn't provided.

CHANGING OIL

Don't change oil with the engine cold. Unless it's been brought up to operating temperature thick, cold oil will cling to engine parts and remain behind to contaminate the new oil. Drive the car to a level place and pull the drain plug immediately. This will guarantee that the dirt particles being held in suspension will drain out with the oil and not settle to the bottom of the crankcase. An old dishpan or a 10-quart oil container with one side cut out will make a good receptacle for catching the oil as it drains.

While the oil is draining, take out the oil filter. Throwaway filters may demand a special tool for their removal, but filters with disposable elements require only an ordinary wrench. Never install a throwaway filter too tightly or it may later prove impossible to take off in one piece. Install the new filter element and, once the drain opening has dripped its last drop, put back the plug and torque it to about 30 foot-pounds. Drain plugs are easily stripped or jammed and may start leaking due to deformation of their gasket if overtightened.

Add the correct quantity of motor oil to the engine and check the dipstick. Don't be surprised if it is slightly above the "FULL" mark since the new filter will absorb at least a pint of oil once the engine is started. Do not accelerate the engine above an idle until the oil pressure gauge registers 20 pounds per square inch or until the oil warning light has gone off for several seconds. After oil has circulated through the engine, shut it off for five minutes and re-check the level to make sure that it's up to the "FULL" line.

That's all there is to the job, yet the steps outlined here are considerably more painstaking than those practiced in most service stations. Filling station attendants often leave cars sitting cold for long periods before draining and draining is seldom complete because they're in a hurry to get another car on the rack. There's a good chance that home oil changes will extend the life of your engine in addition to saving money on oil.

GEAR OIL

Manual transmissions and rear axle gear cases have oil specifications just as the engine does. S.A.E. 90 is usually recommended for year-round use and S.A.E. 80 for service in climates with a great deal of cold weather. Limited slip differentials require special lubricants.

Unfortunately, many service stations use one type of oil for everything that comes into their shop. It's the car owner's responsibility to make sure that his car is getting what it needs. Multi-viscosity S.A.E. 80-90 gear oils are coming into wide use to solve one aspect of the problem, but cars with limited slip differentials must never be filled with ordinary lubricants.

This is the correct amount of lubricant to apply to a distributor cam. Too much may contaminate points, too little will allow the points' rubbing block to wear rapidly.

Most cars are scheduled for a tune-up at the same time as a lube job. Distributor cams need lubing also, and lithium grease or cam grease (capsule) should be used.

GREASE JOBS

Chassis lubrication is fast going the way of the dodo bird. Most late model cars can be driven 100,000 miles without requiring chassis lubrication and without noticeable wear to the steering and suspension parts. If your car has grease fittings and requires periodic chassis lubrication it's entirely practical to do the job yourself. Service stations charge $1.50 to $2.50 for a lube job but the actual cost of the grease can be measured in pennies. A grease gun and a few cartridges of lubricant will therefore pay for itself very quickly.

Wipe each grease fitting clean, then pump grease into it until *new* grease begins oozing from between the parts. Old grease should then be wiped from all parts and fittings. The average service station attendant seldom cleans the fittings and pumps grease only until the old crud starts to move. This may save a few cents worth of grease and keep the floor from getting dirty but it doesn't do anything for the poor car owner who will eventually end up with a worn out suspension system and expensive repairs.

BALL JOINTS

The front suspension ball joints on most American cars have a plug which must be removed to lubricate them. The procedure is to replace the plug with a grease fitting and pump EP (extreme pressure) lubricant into them until it starts to come out of the bleed opening. If the neoprene seal starts to expand, it's filling with grease and the job is done. Some car owners who have become tired of replacing worn-out ball joints simply leave the grease fittings in and lube their cars every 3,000 miles as they did in the "good old days."

UNIVERSAL JOINTS

The U-joints on older cars have grease fittings. In recent years these have been replaced by plugs similar to those described in our discussion of suspension ball joints. Still others must be disassembled for lubrication, an operation described later in this book. Universal joints with plugs can be lubricated exactly as suspension ball joints are.

Distributor spark advance mechanisms need to be lubricated with a few drops of motor oil. Check to see that rubber bumper is still in place on GM Delco distributors.

There are many "oil can" lubrication jobs to be done. These include generator and starter bearings, throttle linkages, the distributor shaft, and the heater controls.

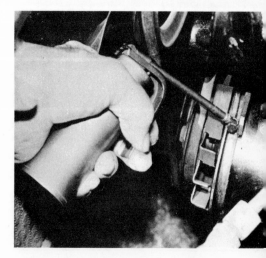

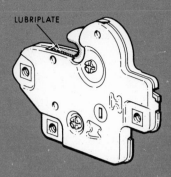

LUBRIPLATE

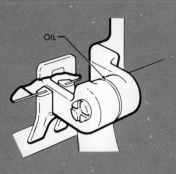

OIL

Trunk latches, door latches, hood latches, and even glove compartment latches need to be lubricated for a long and reliable life. Lubriplate or lithium grease are best.

Hinges on doors or station wagon tailgates should be oiled with motor oil or dripless oil. Exposed hinges on Volkswagens should always receive special care at lube time.

AIR CLEANERS

Oil bath air cleaners are becoming rare, although VW still retains this type. Empty the old oil and wash the unit with kerosene every 12,000 miles, then refill to the line marked on the outer housing with S.A.E. 30 motor oil. Oil-wetted wire mesh air cleaners are found on many older cars, but on no current model. Clean their filter element every 4,000 miles by sloshing it up and down in a pan of kerosene. Pour S.A.E. 30 motor oil over the mesh and allow the excess to drain off. Mesh-filled breather caps should be cleaned in the same way, but not oiled.

Dry and oil-wetted polyurethane filter elements should be washed in clean kerosene and squeezed dry. The oiled type should be dipped into S.A.E. 30 motor oil and squeezed out lightly. Dry paper air cleaner elements should have the dust shaken from them each 6,000 miles and the element replaced after 12,000 miles of service.

OIL CAN JOBS

Generators on older cars have oil cups for both the front and rear armature bearings, but later generators need lubrication at the rear only. Alternators have pre-lubed sealed bearings at both ends. Distributors formerly had an oil cup for lubricating their shaft, but this too has disappeared in recent years. However, most distributors still need to have their advance mechanism oiled during point service. The accelerator linkage, handbrake mechanism, door hinges and latches should also be given a few drops of lubricant at each oil change.

Trunk and hood latches, seat guides, heater cables and dash controls, door hold-open plates may be lubricated with white lithium grease or lubriplate. In general, every moving part on the car requires some form of lubrication. Even windshield wiper shafts should be treated to a few drops of oil periodically.

Performing these service operations yourself means more than just a longer lasting car. They are also valuable preparation for more advanced automotive maintenance work. After a few months doing his own lube jobs and oil changes even the greenest newcomer to auto mechanics is likely to find the mechanical parts of his car a great deal less mysterious and overpowering than they formerly were.

Independent parts jobbers can supply many items for your car that the dealer doesn't stock. Prices are lower than dealers' on most things and guarantees are usually good.

BUYING PARTS

How to get the best deal on new, used or rebuilt automobile parts

Your dealer may be the only available parts source while your car is new, which can be the chanciest proposition since Neal Armstrong picked the site for the first lunar parking lot. Volkswagen is known to charge exceptionally honest prices for replacement parts, but the parts departments of certain low-volume luxury makes are run by some of the most skillful gougers this side of the South China Sea. Most new car agencies try to meet their operating expenses with the profits derived from parts and service. Everything they make selling new cars is sheer gravy. In order to pay the toll, the cost of factory replacement parts is often marked up shamelessly.

PARTS STORES

Auto supply stores (jobbers) can usually provide replacement parts of equal quality at lower cost. They have a mark-up deal going too, and sell parts at a considerably lower price to garages and service stations than they do to ordinary retail customers. Ostensibly this is to promote volume sales, but what it really amounts to is war on the consumer waged under pressure from the service industry. The practice is of questionable legality and despite a Senate committee investigation several years ago which turned up many similar boondoggles in the automobile parts and repair racket, nothing has ever really been done. Nevertheless, a new or rebuilt water pump from an independent jobber will cost less than a similar part from the average dealer.

Stores which are a part of an auto store chain and which market everything from toys at Christmas to lawnmowers in the summer are another source of replacement parts. The prices are lower and definitely more honest, but in some cases quality does suffer. It's a good idea to inspect the original part carefully, then take a close look at what the auto store is offering. If it's noticeably shoddy by comparison it may be better to look elsewhere than to take a chance. However, if quick low-cost repairs are the idea, "Main Street" auto stores are the best.

Salvage yards which specialize in used car parts are fine places to save big money when a new engine or transmission is required. Parts are carefully catalogued and labeled.

MAIL ORDERS

If you can afford a few days delay, shop for replacement parts at Sears. In most cases they'll have such things as starters, carburetors, and water pumps in stock. Pistons, connecting rods, and other less frequently requested items may have to be shipped from a warehouse. Delivery is fairly prompt, the guarantee good, and quality generally satisfactory.

Mail order companies much as J.C. Whitney and Honest Charley offer a wide variety of parts at the fairest possible prices. Delivery tends to be slow on some items so, if you're planning to drive the car to Aculpulco in two days, forget it. The cheapest items listed are sometimes of inferior quality, so it's better to select from their "premium" priced lines.

REBUILDS

Shops specializing in rebuilt parts especially electrical components—are something of a mixed bag. Unless they offer a good guarantee and a liberal trade in on your old parts it may be better to shop for an all-new replacement.

The word "rebuilding" can cover a multitude of sins (or virtues). Find out if starter windings have been replaced or whether the old ones have been patched up, painted, and a few mechanical components renewed. You can do that kind of "rebuilding" with a little electrical know-how and a mail order repair kit.

WRECKERS

Not all wrecking yards are good parts sources. Some wreckers are strictly in the scrap business and are not interested in the resale of auto parts. Others operate from farm pastures in rural areas and permit the buyer to locate and remove his own parts. You can usually haggle for a good price.

Large auto wreckers keep supplies of used parts on shelves in their warehouse for immediate sale. They'll charge their own price, but also agree to take back any faulty parts they may have gotten past their inspection. You can save a great deal on such assemblies as transmissions, rear ends, cylinder head or complete engines from these dealers.

PARTS NOMENCLATURE

One thing's a "must"; *know exactly what you're after* when you buy parts.

Whenever possible, take along the old part for comparison and identification. Write down your car's serial number, engine number, model designation and body style. Record the number stamped on any part that can't be taken with you. Be specific in filling out blanks on mail order forms. Describe the part accurately as "a front crankshaft mainbearing oil seal for a 1965 327 Chevrolet V-8 engine" and not merely as "a Chevy oil seal." NOTE: Make it easy on the parts man and he might give you a "professional" discount!

ENGINE TUNE-UPS

Here's how to handle the most important phase of auto maintenance

A few years ago a major spark plug manufacturer conducted an advertising campaign with the slogan "An Untuned Car Is Trouble." Alas, truer words were never spoken. If every car on the highway received a complete tune-up each 10,000 miles there would be a virtual end to cars that refuse to start, millions of dollars worth of gasoline saved and a very worthwhile reduction in air pollution levels.

SPARK PLUGS

Because they have the roughest job in an engine, spark plugs are the heart of every tune-up. Their electrodes begin eroding due to high voltages and combustion heat from the moment they are placed in service. This causes the center and side electrodes to assume a worn, rounded appearance and the gap between to grow by about .001" every 1,000 miles.

Very high voltages are needed to ionize the air in a plug gap so that a spark may arc across it. Ionization is promoted by sharp-cornered electrodes and fairly narrow gaps. Several thousand additional volts are needed to fire a plug with worn electrodes and, after 5,000 or 6,000 miles of service, plugs often begin to operate unreliably when the available voltage is low or when cylinder pressures are exceptionally high. Starting may therefore become difficult and the engine often "misses" during hard acceleration.

After 5,000 or 6,000 miles of service, spark plugs should be removed from the engine and re-gapped to their original specifications. A round wire gauge is best for this purpose since it conforms better to worn electrodes than does a flat feeler gauge. After 10,000 or 12,000 miles of service the plugs should be replaced with new ones.

Badly worn engines and high-performance engines which are seldom used at full power often accumulate a considerable load of deposits on the firing ends of their spark plugs. Sand-blast cleaning, as practiced in most service stations, is of questionable value since it increases the voltage required to fire the plugs by further rounding the electrodes. Also, mechanics will sometimes "pre-clean" the plugs with a wire brush which may leave conductive "pencil lines" on the insulator that will later cause the plug to short and misfire. If you have your plugs sand blasted take time to file the end of the center electrode flat so that its edges are sharp and square. This is a good practice whether the plug has been cleaned or not and is a worthwhile addition to your re-gapping operation. Plugs can also be cleaned at home using solvent and a sharp wooden stick.

Different engines require different plugs. Every major spark plug manufacturer has developed plugs designed particularly for the engine in your car, but steer clear of re-manufactured and off-brand replacements. Tell the parts man

Gapping spark plugs is one of the vital little tasks that go into a tune-up. New plugs are needed every 10,000 to 12,000 miles and these should be gapped also (to make sure.)

These diagrams explain the relationship of dwell to distributor point gap. A dwell meter will check the gap quickly and with ease, but a feeler gauge is as accurate.

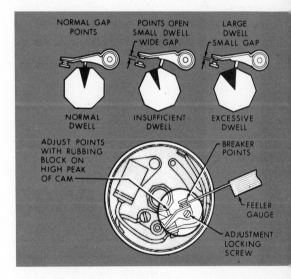

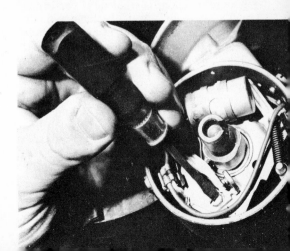

The first step when adjusting distributor point gap is to loosen the screw locking the breaker assembly to the distributor's advance plate. Locations will vary slightly.

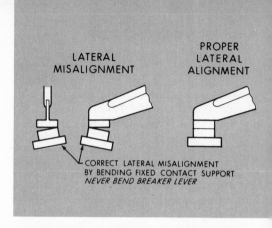

LATERAL
MISALIGNMENT

PROPER
LATERAL
ALIGNMENT

CORRECT LATERAL MISALIGNMENT
BY BENDING FIXED CONTACT SUPPORT
NEVER BEND BREAKER LEVER

Select the feeler gauge thickness which meets the car's specifications and turn the engine to open points. Move points to obtain correct gap, tighten lock screw.

Even brand new point assemblies may not be in perfect alignment. If not they will wear prematurely. Bend stationary contact to correct any misalignment which exists.

the year, make, model, and engine type for your car and he will locate the correct plug for your engine in his specification book.

Make sure that the plug holes are clean and lubricate the threads of the new spark plugs lightly before installing them. New plugs are gapped at the factory, but check them anyway to make sure that they match the specifications given in your owner's manual. Torque plugs to 20 or 25 foot-pounds, or about one-half turn after they are finger-tight. Over-tightening may ruin the gaskets.

THE DISTRIBUTOR

"Tune-up kits" consisting of a new distributor rotor, condenser and point set are sold by practically every store with an automotive department. This along with a new set of plugs is what most car owners call a "tune-up." Actually, factory-quality condensers seldom go bad and distributor rotors are usually good for at least 50,000 miles. These items are often replaced quite needlessly. Unless the rotor is conspicuously worn or a test at the local auto store shows your condenser to be faulty, there's no reason why they should be replaced.

Distributor points need to be checked at least once every 10,000 miles to make sure that they are not seriously burned

and that their gap hasn't narrowed due to rubbing block wear. Narrow point gaps are responsible for a great deal of hard starting, stalling, and cars that suddenly cease running in traffic. A flat feeler gauge should be used to adjust the point gap after first turning the engine with the starter so that the rubbing block of the movable contact arm is atop one of the "bumps" on the distributor cam.

Gapping the points with a feeler gauge can be a genuine pain in the neck on some engines. Dwell meters have therefore come into wide use for checking distributor point adjustment. Although they cost between $10 and $25, depending on quality, they are easy to use. The red lead on the meter should be clipped onto the ignition coil terminal which receives a small wire coming from the side of the distributor. Connect the black lead to "ground" somewhere on the engine and turn the meter's selector to the number of cylinders.

Operate the engine at an idle. The needle should indicate a reading that is within the specifications listed for your car. New points must still be given a preliminary feeler gauge gapping before they can be tested with a dwell meter. Nevertheless, a meter makes it a lot easier to keep track of points that are already in service.

Most cars must have their engines

In recent years all car makers have begun using point assemblies rather than point sets that must be installed piece by piece in the distributor. Note good alignment.

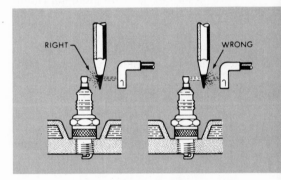

The high tension and spark plug cables are overlooked at tune-up time and cause many "mysterious" misses later on. An ohmmeter is needed to check modern resistance cable.

switched off and the distributor cap removed so that the point adjustment can be altered. The cap must then be replaced and the engine started for another dwell test. However, GM and AM cars with Delco ignition are fitted with what is known as a "window" distributor. This unit permits dwell adjustments to be made while the engine is running. The meter's needle can therefore be "tuned in" 'til it's right on the money.

When installing new points or a condenser, make certain that the floor of the distributor and the part of the condenser or point assembly that comes into contact with it are clean and free of oil. Good electrical contact is a "must." In fact, most burned and pitted points are not caused by faulty condensers, but by poor contact between the condenser's case and the distributor.

The distributor cam should be lubricated with white lithium or special cam grease. These lubricants are not so likely to splash onto the points and cause burning. Lubricate the advance mechanism sparingly with motor oil and inspect the distributor cap to make sure it's clean and free of cracks or carbon tracks.

IGNITION WIRES

Faulty plug cables can cause more trouble than a jar of lightning bugs let

Whenever the ignition coil is removed for testing or replacement there is a chance that its small wires will be reversed. Spark should flare between pencil and the plug.

Inexpensive neon timing lights like this are fine for home service, but require a darkened room for their weak flash. No. 1 plug fires through unit to produce light.

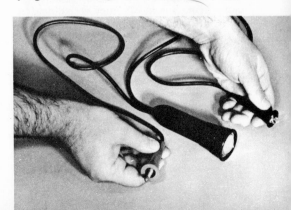

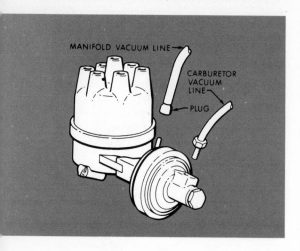

MANIFOLD VACUUM LINE →

CARBURETOR
VACUUM
LINE →

← PLUG

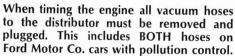

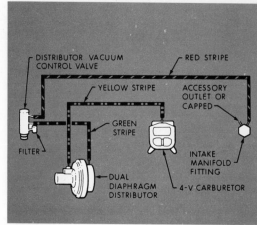

DISTRIBUTOR VACUUM
CONTROL VALVE

RED STRIPE

YELLOW STRIPE

ACCESSORY
OUTLET OR
CAPPED

GREEN
STRIPE

FILTER →

INTAKE
MANIFOLD
FITTING

DUAL
DIAPHRAGM
DISTRIBUTOR

4-V CARBURETOR

When timing the engine all vacuum hoses to the distributor must be removed and plugged. This includes BOTH hoses on Ford Motor Co. cars with pollution control.

The vacuum lines controlling spark advance on Ford Motor Company cars with IMCO are shown here. Unless all are in perfectly sound condition faulty advance results.

loose in a planatarium, yet they're probably the most frequently overlooked part of a tune-up. All new cars are equipped with non-metallic radio resistance cables. These bits of glamourized spaghetti won't carry enough current to light a flashlight bulb, but their carbon-impregnated core is conductive enough to provide a path for high-voltage spark impulses to travel along.

There are good resistance cables and bad resistance cables. Unfortunately, about 90% of the world's car makers have stuck with the bad stuff even though several types are available which are impossible to fault. Belden IRS cable is the best. It has a continuous conductive rubber-like extruded tube through its center which cannot be damaged by rough handling or deliberate abuse. It also offers a fool-proof terminal system. Packard Radio TV Suppression cable ranks very close to it, but most other resistance cables on the market are strictly also-rans.

Check the plugs and cables with a spark plug tester or check the cables with an ohmmeter at each tune-up or at the first sign of misfiring. If a cable is not firing regularly, or if it tests above 4,000 ohms per foot or over 20,000 ohms for any individual cable, it's time for a new set of cables. Don't switch to metallic core

cables. They'll not only cause enough radio interference to get you into a "fix" with the "fuzz," but will probably cause added spark plug erosion as well.

THE COIL

Don't forget the ignition coil when you do a tune-up. Make sure its nose is clean and that the nipple over the high tension cable fits tightly. You can test the coil by removing the high tension cable from the center of the distributor cap and holding it about ¼-inch from a grounded place on the engine. Grip it with a wooden or plastic clothes pin to avoid electrical shocks.

Have somebody run the starter and observe the spark that jumps between the cable to "ground." If it's bright blue and snaps loudly, your coil is in good shape. A yellow spark indicates low voltage and a coil that's getting weak. If the spark won't jump ¼-inch, you'd better start walking toward the parts store for a new coil, 'cause the one you have might not even start the engine!

TIMING

Hook your timing light up to the #1 cylinder's spark plug lead as described in the instructions packaged with the light. The vacuum hose should be disconnected from the distributor. Late Chrysler Corporation engines may be fitted with a solenoid distributor having a plastic box beside the vacuum diaphragm. The small wire leading to this box should be disconnected along with the vacuum hose. Do this when checking dwell also. Remove both hoses on late Ford engines with dual vacuum distributors. Always plug vacuum hoses which are removed during timing operations on any engine.

Loosen the distributor hold-down bolt slightly so that the distributor body can just barely be turned by hand. Let the engine idle and aim the timing light at the timing marks on the engine. These are usually located on the crankshaft pully, so be careful of the spinning fan. Move the distributor from side to side until the timing marks line up in the correct position. Tighten the distributor hold-down, and you're ready to re-connect the vacuum lines and move on to the next phase of your tune-up.

VALVE ADJUSTMENT

If your engine has hydraulic lifters you can usually forget about valve adjust-ments during a tune-up. Adjustments are a "must" on engines with mechanical lifters, and on Volkswagens they're a matter of life or death. Remove the valve cover(s) and distributor cap. The engine must be turned by hand or with the starter until the distributor cam is just about to open the points. Check the position of the rotor against the wires on the distributor cap to determine which cylinder is about to fire. Adjust that cylinder's valves, then turn the engine until the rotor is aligned with the next cylinder in the firing order and the points are about to open. Adjust the valves of that cylinder and continue until all cylinders have been done. Many car owners prefer to adjust the valves while the spark plugs are out for re-gapping since it makes the engine easier to turn and stop in the right position.

Valve adjustments must be made according to the specifications listed in your car owner's manual. Some engines should have their valves adjusted while the engine is hot, others with the engine completely cold. Exhaust valves normally require a wider gap than intakes. You can tell one from the other by looking at the intake and exhaust manifolds to see which parts the individual valve lines up with. Usually there's an exhaust valve at

Here's what the FoMoCo IMCO advance system looks like in real life. Valve in engine block advances spark if engine overheats. Extra hose used with air conditioning.

Beginning with the 1970 models, Chrysler Corporation cars with big engine options got this solenoid-controlled spark advance unit. Remove wire and hose for timing.

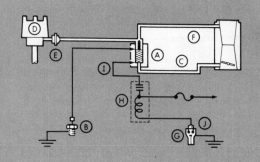

Recent General Motors cars with automatic transmission have had this transmission-controlled spark circuit. "B" is switch in transmission that limits advance in low gears. "A" is the solenoid, "F" and "C" are vacuum lines to carb. Only hose "E" needs to be removed and plugged while the car's distributor ("D") is being re-timed.

the end of the head, then two intakes, and then two exhausts, two intakes *etc.*, until you reach a final single exhaust valve at the other end of the head.

Select the two blades on your feeler gauge which match the engine's specifications. Insert the correct gauge between the valve stem and the rocker arm. If it slides in easily and can be moved around with just noticeable drag, the valve is in proper adjustment. If the gauge will not go in, or if it fits loosely within the gap, the valve needs adjusting.

A majority of engines have a lock nut holding the adjustment screw in place. This must be loosened slightly so that the screw can be turned and re-tightened when the correct gap has been achieved. The job can be a bit tricky the first time you try it, so *always* re-check the gap after the lock nut has been tightened. Many domestic cars now have self-locking adjusting screws which make the job much easier.

Here's the solenoid in General Motors' TCS (Transmission Controlled Spark) setup. A check of its wires and hoses is in order at tune-up time lest something be adrift.

Distributor point dwell can be adjusted in GM cars with the engine running, thanks to this "window" distributor. Hook up dwell meter, insert Allen wrench and twist away.

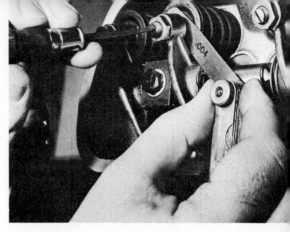

Thanks to hydraulic lifters, valve lash adjustments at tune-up time are virtually a thing of the past. First step in making adjustments is to loosen rocker arm nut.

The cylinder must be in position to fire, so check the distributor rotor's position. Turn the adjusting screw until the correct feeler gauge moves about with slight drag.

Hold the adjuster in position and tighten the lock nut. This may take some practice until you get it right. Do not overdo the tightening bit or you'll strip the threads.

After tightening the lock nut test the gap with a feeler gauge that's .002″ oversize. If this will enter the gap it is too wide and the space adjustment should be done over.

FUEL SYSTEM

Inspect the fuel pump and lines at each tune-up to detect any leaks which may have developed. If the fuel pump has a built-in filter now's the time to clean it. In-line filters should be serviced as required. Look for leaks around the carburetor hold-down nuts and check the screws that hold the top onto the carburetor for tightness.

EMISSION CONTROL

Air injection systems should have their filter replaced or cleaned as required. All engines now have positive crankcase ventilation systems, so clean the valve in solvent at each tune-up and install a new one at the interval recommended by the car manufacturer.

Cars built since 1968 have closed PCV systems. Here's a quick check that will

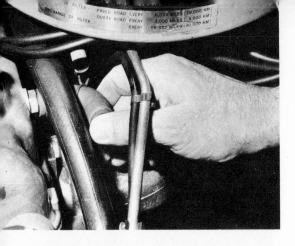

Check the crankcase ventilation system by removing hose leading from valve cover to air cleaner. There should be suction. If not, replace hose, take off oil filler cap.

If vacuum draws paper against filler the flame arresting screen in the air cleaner or hose is clogged. If not, the positive crankcase ventilation valve is at fault.

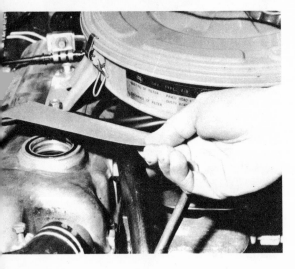

If emission control hoses aren't leaking and carb still won't adjust it may be time for a cleaning and rebuild. Carb rebuild kits like that shown are readily available.

tell you if they are working right: (1) With the engine idling, remove the hose from the rocker arm cover and place your thumb over the end. There should be definite suction and loss of engine speed. (2) If no suction is felt, remove the oil filler cap and replace the hose. Hold a piece of stiff paper loosely over the oil filler pipe. After a few seconds, the tag should be drawn against the filler pipe with noticeable force. If it is, the flame arrester screen in the hose leading the air cleaner is probably clogged. If it is not drawn against the pipe, the PCV valve is probably clogged.

CARBURETOR ADJUSTMENT

Turning the idle adjustment(s) on the carburetor should produce a noticeable change in engine speed and operation. If it doesn't, the carburetor is undoubtedly due for a cleaning or rebuild. The classic method for adjusting the idle is to turn the mixture screw in until the engine begins to falter. Note the position of the screw, then turn it counterclockwise until the engine again "rolls" or loses speed. The correct setting is usually about midway between these two positions.

A vacuum gauge makes the job more precise. Connect the gauge to the engine's manifold vacuum port and adjust the idle screws until the maximum vacuum read-

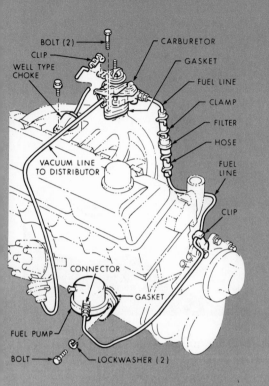

BOLT (2)

CLIP

WELL TYPE
CHOKE

CARBURETOR

GASKET

FUEL LINE

CLAMP

FILTER

HOSE

FUEL
LINE

VACUUM LINE
TO DISTRIBUTOR

CLIP

CONNECTOR

GASKET

FUEL PUMP

BOLT

LOCKWASHER (2)

Check the fuel system before adjusting the carb. Some late emission control engines have no carb adjustments, or have a limited adjustment range. Here's typical layout.

Beginning in 1971 new cars have a system to prevent air pollution caused by fuel evaporation. Vapor line and carb vent line enter PCV system. Check for bad hoses.

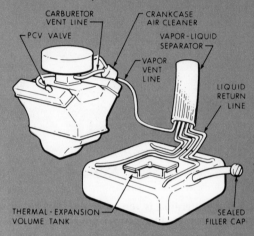

CARBURETOR
VENT LINE

CRANKCASE
AIR CLEANER

PCV VALVE

VAPOR-LIQUID
SEPARATOR

VAPOR
VENT
LINE

LIQUID
RETURN
LINE

THERMAL-EXPANSION
VOLUME TANK

SEALED
FILLER CAP

ing is obtained. Adjust one screw at a time on V-8 engines, going back and forth between the two adjustments. Multiple carburetors should be set with the help of a Uni-Syn, or other multiple carburetor synchronizing tool.

On engines with exhaust emission controls there may be plastic stops on the idle needles to limit their travel or, in some cases, no adjustment at all. Most emission controlled engines should not be set for maximum vacuum or "best idle." Check the service manual for your car to find the correct vacuum specifications and stick to them. Some car makers give such idle adjustment specifications as 1.5% to 2.5% CO (carbon monoxide). It requires an expensive exhaust gas analyzer to check this accurately. What it means, however, is to set the adjustment near its lean limit. Smog laws or not, there are relatively few service departments that

use, or even have analyzing equipment.

If the idle speed of the engine is too fast or too slow after adjustment, the throttle stop screw must be adjusted to bring the idle into the correct speed range. Cars with automatic transmissions should be in "drive" with the parking brake set during carb adjustments. After the correct speed is obtained, the idle mixture adjusting screws must once again be adjusted.

That's it for the tune-up. Certain other operations should take place at this time such as a compression check, battery test, and cooling system inspected. Many service stations offer a "$9.95" tune-up which is really just a plug cleaning and point adjustment job. If you want the kind of tune-up outlined here you can count on at least a $25 bill. For that kind of money it's probably worth taking all of Saturday morning to do it yourself!

Expert attention is required at regular intervals to obtain proper battery life. Yet there are many things the car owner can do that will prevent, or curtail, electrical failures.

BATTERIES AND CHARGING

Proper care means a longer, more productive life for your battery

Many motorists fall victim to battery trouble merely because they have the wrong idea of how a battery works. Ask the average driver what his battery does and he'll probably tell you that it stores electricity. Regardless of how often you've heard this lie, *don't believe it.*

Batteries aren't banks, they're factories. Their purpose is to manufacture electrical current using a special chemical process. When you turn the key to operate the starter, sulphuric acid combines with the lead plates inside the battery's cells partially converting them to lead sulphate and giving off a bundle of usable electrons in the process. The electrolyte solution in the battery is mostly water and when all the acid has been used up its potential for producing electricity stops.

If electrical current from the car's charging system is routed into the battery the electro-chemical reaction is reversed and the lead sulphate changes back into lead and lead dioxide, freeing sulphuric acid which returns to solution in the electrolyte. If people would treat their batteries like chemistry sets instead of savings accounts, there'd be fewer failures.

REGULATORS

Cars with generators have regulators. Cars with alternators have regulators too,

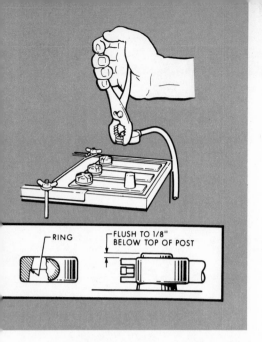

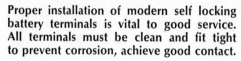

RING

FLUSH TO 1/8"
BELOW TOP OF POST

Proper installation of modern self locking battery terminals is vital to good service. All terminals must be clean and fit tight to prevent corrosion, achieve good contact.

This battery delivered five years of good service but a hydrometer check shows that it's all over now. Readings below 1.200 mean cells are weak or badly discharged.

but they're usually much smaller and are sometimes built into the alternator itself rather than existing as a separate unit. In recent years the trend has been to manufacture regulators as sealed units. These cannot be adjusted and must be replaced when faulty. Actually, this isn't a bad idea since improperly adjusted regulators have probably wiped out more batteries than the British Navy.

AMMETERS

Unfortunately, another modern trend has worked against the best interests of the battery; namely, the change to "idiot lights." One of the biggest favors a driver can do his car is to install an ammeter whenever the factory has neglected to provide one. Such an instrument is your first line of defense against unexpected battery failures.

Because most people think their battery is "storing" electricity, they assume that it's a good sign when the ammeter shows a healthy charge. It's not. As a

matter of fact, it's an almost sure sign that the battery is approaching the end of its useful life. A closer look at what really goes on inside the battery and charging systems will show why.

The battery must supply all the electrical current it takes to start your car. This means that some of the acid in the electrolyte must combine chemically with the lead in the battery plates. However, once the engine has started the charging system begins to function. The alternator takes over the job of operating the engine's ignition system, the headlights, radio and any other electrical accessories that happen to be in use.

Meanwhile, the regulator senses that the battery isn't at its maximum strength. If cars still had hand cranks you might feel a little undernourished too! In correcting this condition the regulator sends electrical current from the alternator into the battery, thereby reversing the electrochemical process and returning sulphuric acid to solution with the electrolyte. If necessary, the regulator will step up the

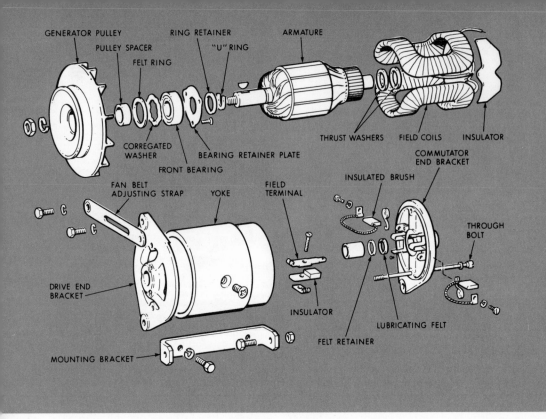

GENERATOR PULLEY
PULLEY SPACER
FELT RING
RING RETAINER
"U" RING
ARMATURE
CORREGATED WASHER
BEARING RETAINER PLATE
FRONT BEARING
THRUST WASHERS
FIELD COILS
INSULATOR
COMMUTATOR END BRACKET
INSULATED BRUSH
FAN BELT ADJUSTING STRAP
YOKE
FIELD TERMINAL
THROUGH BOLT
DRIVE END BRACKET
INSULATOR
LUBRICATING FELT
FELT RETAINER
MOUNTING BRACKET

Exploded view shows parts of a typical DC generator. Note location and installation of brushes. These are the generator parts that car owners need to replace most frequently.

alternator's output to carry added load.

Because current is flowing into the battery, the ammeter indicates a charge condition. But after a few miles of driving, the battery should have been restored to full strength and the ammeter needle returned to "zero." This shows that the battery is fully charged and that the alternator is handling the car's electrical load all by itself. If the ammeter constantly reads in the "charge" range it usually means that the battery is weak and can no longer attain the level of power that it was designed to produce.

When your car's ammeter starts showing a constant charge reading it's time to test the battery. If you don't have an ammeter, it's a good idea to give the battery a weekly hydrometer check anyway. This is the most accurate way to determine the charge level of its cells. If the battery is fully charged and the ammeter persists with its high reading it's a sign that the regulator is at fault.

TESTING

A battery hydrometer measures the specific gravity of the electrolyte. Pure water has a specific gravity of 1.000. Sulphuric acid is heavier. The more acid in the battery water, the higher the electrolyte's specific gravity.

The specific gravity of the electrolyte is about 1.280 in a fully charged cell. A reading of 1.250 is considered good, 1.225 and 1.250 is fair, and anything below that is definitely poor. If the specific gravity of any cell is less than 1.150, the battery is for all practical purposes deader than Great Caeser's kidneys.

The temperature of the electrolyte has a definite influence on hydrometer readings. A thermometer can be inserted into the electrolyte if you want to be dead accurate. At 80 Fahrenheit your hydrometer's scale will be correct. For every 10° above 80° .004 must be added to the

New brushes must be sanded to conform to the commutator. Place the rough side of the sandpaper against brush, then turn it with the commutator 'til the brush fits.

Alternator brushes usually remove along with their holder. Some small alternators must be disassembled for brush replacement but most do not. Brush trouble is rare.

reading. Subtract .004 for every 10° below 80°.

All cells should receive a hydrometer test at each tune-up and whenever the ammeter begins behaving suspiciously. Not correcting an overcharge is like sentencing your battery to death in the hot seat. Catch the problem early enough and you'll have a $5 regulator to replace instead of a $30 battery.

DISCHARGES

When the ammeter indicates a discharge it shows that the charging system is unable to handle the electrical system's load and requires help from the battery. This usually occurs only when a great many electrical accessories are in use with the engine idling. If this is so, the ammeter will return to "zero" as the engine speeds up, or go into the charge range for a short time and then drop back once the battery has been returned to full power.

If the ammeter spends a great deal of time in the discharge range, then shows a constant charge when the engine speeds up, your battery may never be getting up to full strength. Check it with a hydrometer, and if the cells are low, you'd better cut out listening to the radio and running the heater while idling in traffic. Batteries that are never fully charged develop a condition called "sulphating"

which can permanently cripple or destroy them.

If the ammeter needle starts moving back and forth proportional to engine speed, going deep into the discharge range while idling and far up into the charge range when the engine is speeded up, you have a dead regulator. Replace it immediately or you'll have a ruined battery too.

BATTERY CARE

Even though your car's ammeter always reads a nice healthy "zero" and only makes brief excursions into the "charge" range after starting, there are still many things that can be done to make your battery live longer. Regular hydrometer checks and keeping the electrolyte level up to the "full" indicators built into the top of each cell are the first step. This will help the battery's chemical processes to remain uniform.

You must also keep the cells *chemically pure*. Service stations normally use ordinary tap water in batteries, so don't let them get near yours. Fill it yourself using *distilled water only*. It sells for 50¢ to 60¢ a gallon at your neighborhood super market which is a very small price to pay for the added months of life it can give the cells. Iron, chlorides and manganese can be seriously harmful even in

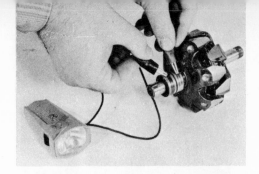

Diodes can be tested with ohmmeter or low-powered test light. Current should flow when probes are touched to lead wire and case, but not when they are reversed.

Broken or burned out field windings can be detected by applying a test light to the rotor's slip rings as shown. The lamp should light, but dimly due to resistance.

Grounded field windings can also cause an alternator to go bad. When a test light is connected to the slip rings and to the shaft the light should not come on at all.

Grounded windings in generator armatures are a very common problem. There should be no electrical contact between the unit's shaft and the brass bars on the commutator.

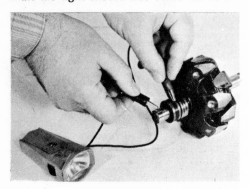

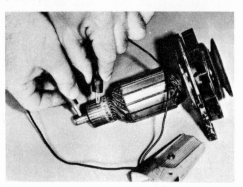

small concentrations. These things are common in tap water and remain behind to form a progressive build-up as water evaporates from the battery. Battery manufacturers sometimes say that distilled water isn't necessary. Frankly, I suspect their motives.

CHARGING TROUBLE

If the generator warning light comes on and stays on, or if the ammeter suddenly plunges into the discharge zone and stays there, you have charging system trouble. If the water temperature starts to climb at the same time, stop immediately. Your fan belt has broken. But, if the generator or alternator is running and there's still no charge you're going to have to look elsewhere.

On cars with generators the problem

is often worn brushes. If the generator has inspection holes try pressing the brushes tighter against the rotating commutator with the tip of a screwdriver. Should this cause the ammeter to jump into the "charge" zone the trouble is definitely brushes. You can install replacements yourself but if the commutator is worn, or "wobbles" as the armature is turned, the unit must be taken to an automotive machine shop to have the commutator turned.

Alternators seldom have brush problems. Nevertheless, their brushes are very easy to replace. Some alternators have an isolation diode either in the regulator or on the alternator's case which prevents electrical current of reversed polarity from entering the unit. Reversed polarity occurs when "positive" current is accidently routed to the negative wire and

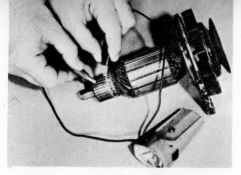

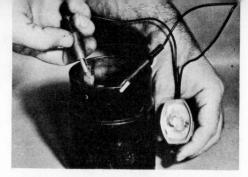

Individual windings sometimes come loose from the commutator bars. There should be continuity (dim light) between any bar and the one adjacent. If not there is trouble.

Burned out generator windings can be found by attaching one test clip to the field terminal and the other to the generator's frame. The light should come on dimly.

"negative" current has found its way to the positive wire. This can seriously damage an alternator. Carelessly hooked-up battery booster cables are a common cause of such accidents.

Test the isolation diode as shown. It should pass current in one direction only. If it passes no current, or passes current in both directions it is faulty. There are a number of other things which can go wrong with generators and alternators. Test procedures are shown in the photos which will locate most common ailments.

No-charge or low-charge troubles can be caused by faulty regulators too. If your car has a generator rather than the more up-to-date alternator there's an easy test you can make to find out whether the generator or the regulator is at fault.

All you have to do is ground the generator's *field terminal*. There are two or three wires going to the generator and one of them is attached to the field terminal. If there's a radio interference condenser attached to one of the terminals it IS NOT the field terminal. The field terminal usually has an insulating washer around it and many generators have the word "Field" or the letter "F" stamped next to it. If you can find the field terminal on the regulator you can ground the field at that point instead.

Merely take the end of a screwdriver and short between the field terminal and the generator's case or another "grounded" location on the car. If grounding the field produces no change the generator is at fault. Never do this with an alternator system. In fact, never ground, short or re-

verse *any* of the wires associated with an alternator system.

MECHANICAL ILLS

Generators and alternators sometimes break down mechanically, bearing trouble being rather common. Kits are available for rebuilding generators and alternators, or you may be able to trade the old dynamo on a new or rebuilt unit. When fan belts break with suspicious frequency—particularly during high speed travel—suspect an out-of-balance alternator rotor.

Overtightened fan belts are the cause of most pulley and bearing failures. The belt should be adjusted loosely enough that it can be deflected about ½" by pressing against it with the finger tips. Making it any tighter will do more harm than good, but a belt that's loose enough to slip can cause a low-charge condition.

CHARGERS

Battery chargers are fine, but they're no substitute for a healthy battery and charging system. Avoid quick charges. They'll ruin sulphated batteries that might be restored by "trickle" charging.

Watch your ammeter, perform frequent hydrometer checks and keep the electrolyte as pure as a tinsel angel. Do this conscientiously and your battery should still be around after four year's service. Over-charge it, let the electrolyte get low, then fill it up with tap water and you might end up digging a hole for it before its second birthday.

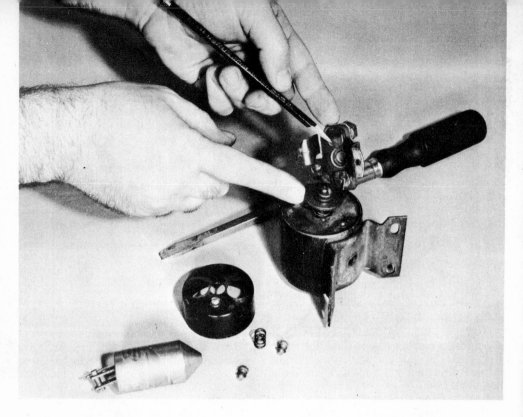

Many starting system failures originate in the solenoid. Most solenoids can be fixed merely by taking them apart and reversing their disc and contacts to restore contact.

THE STARTING SYSTEM

Every driver should know what to do when his car refuses to start

The main components of the starting system are the battery and the starter motor itself. Linking them is a heavy cable which passes through a magnetic switch or solenoid. Also attached to the solenoid are one or two smaller wires. One of these is the starter control wire coming from the ignition switch.

If the starter motor cranks the engine over vigorously, yet the engine refuses to "catch," it is very doubtful that the trouble is in the starting system. Starting system failures usually manifest themselves as a refusal for the starter to crank the engine or to only crank it slowly. If turning the ignition key to the "start" position produces no reaction at all, the starting system is likely to be at fault. But until

you do some accurate troubleshooting don't rule out the possibility that the trouble may be in the ignition switch.

Don't despair when the starting system lets you down. The trouble can often be corrected once you know where it is. In any case, locating the actual source of the malfunction is always the prerequisite.

The battery should be the first item checked. If it is not producing adequate power there is little use in testing other components in the system. A hydrometer test is the best way to determine if the battery is in an adequate state of charge, but when you're stranded in an alley in Perth Amboy and your hydrometer is at home in Hackensack, you'll have to resort to other troubleshooting techniques.

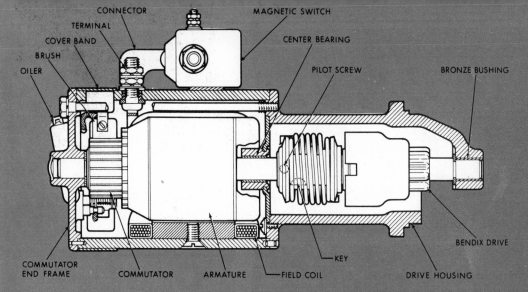

CONNECTOR

TERMINAL

COVER BAND

BRUSH

OILER

MAGNETIC SWITCH

CENTER BEARING

PILOT SCREW

BRONZE BUSHING

COMMUTATOR END FRAME

COMMUTATOR

ARMATURE

FIELD COIL

KEY

DRIVE HOUSING

BENDIX DRIVE

No domestic auto manufacturer uses Bendex starter drives any more but several import brands do. Few of the foreign units are as strongly constructed as the unit shown here.

Overrunning clutch starters have a fork that engages them positively using the energy of the movable solenoid core. Note that the starter shown includes a reduction gear.

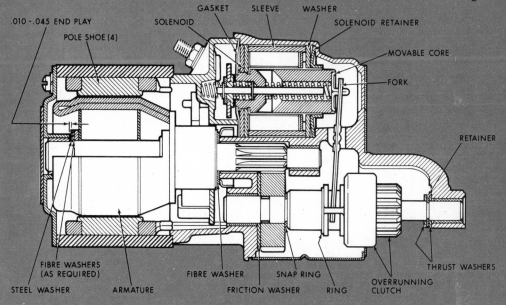

.010 -.045 END PLAY

POLE SHOE (4)

GASKET

SOLENOID

SLEEVE

WASHER

SOLENOID RETAINER

MOVABLE CORE

FORK

RETAINER

FIBRE WASHERS (AS REQUIRED)

STEEL WASHER

ARMATURE

FIBRE WASHER

SNAP RING

FRICTION WASHER

RING

OVERRUNNING CLUTCH

THRUST WASHERS

HEADLIGHT TESTS

Starting troubles can often be traced with the help of your car's lighting system. Switch on the headlights and attempt to operate the starter. One of three things will happen. (1) The lights may go out and the starter fail to operate; (2) the starter will make some sound but the lights dim; (3) the headlights may be bright but no cranking takes place.

If the headlights go out when the starter is used there's probably a poor connection between the battery and the starter

Even the magnetic switches on Ford autos can have their contacts turned for added service, but you'll have to drill out the cover rivets and replace them with screws.

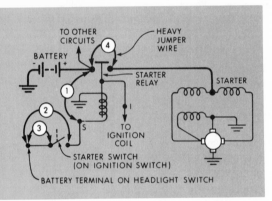

These four jumper cable tests can pinpoint most starting failures. If test #4 won't run starter either the starter motor is at fault or the car's battery is totally dead.

In addition to the solenoid there are one or two other switches in the circuit that controls the starter; the neutral safety switch and the dashboard ignition switch.

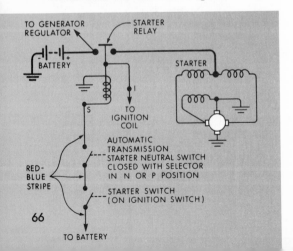

TO GENERATOR REGULATOR
STARTER RELAY
BATTERY
STARTER
TO IGNITION COIL
S
RED-BLUE STRIPE
AUTOMATIC TRANSMISSION STARTER NEUTRAL SWITCH CLOSED WITH SELECTOR IN N OR P POSITION
STARTER SWITCH (ON IGNITION SWITCH)
TO BATTERY

motor. Corroded battery terminals often cause such trouble. If the headlights are extremely dim even before the starter is tried, the battery is probably discharged. Corroded terminals might still be the trouble, however. Sometimes cleaning the terminals and battery posts will get you started when the poor connection has not significantly reduced the ability for the charging system to keep the battery active. A chronically high ammeter reading may be an indication that the battery terminals need attention.

If the engine cranks slowly and the headlights dim noticeably the battery may be low or something is placing an unusual load on the starter. If a hydrometer check has already shown the battery to be at or near full charge you can definitely suspect the latter. A high-viscosity oil in the crankcase may be the trouble in cold weather. If the engine is new or has just been overhauled it's probably an indication that the car needs a cool-off period before restarting. A faulty distributor or improper timing may also have advanced the spark excessively so that early ignition is fighting the action of the starter. Serious engine problems such as a leaking head gasket or stuck carburetor float may have filled the cylinders with water or fuel causing hydrostatic lock.

If the lights stay bright and still there's no response from the starter there's probably an open circuit somewhere in the starting system. This could be anything from a loose wire on the ignition switch to worn-out brushes in the starter motor. If there's a clicking sound from the magnetic switch or solenoid, but the starter does not run, you can be certain that the trouble is in the solenoid's contacts, the starter motor, or starter drive mechanism.

JUMPER TESTS

Locate the solenoid. It may be atop the starter or there may be a separate magnetic switch bolted to the car's body. It has a heavy cable leading to it from the battery and another which extends from another of its terminals to the starter motor. By shunting across the two heavy terminals on the solenoid or magnetic switch you should be able to make the

Next to worn brushes the most common form of starter trouble is grounded or burned-out windings. Check for armature grounds using the test shown.

starter operate if the solenoid or switch is at fault. If the starter still doesn't work the starter motor will have to be disassembled for some of the internal tests illustrated in the photos.

Sometimes a starter motor will run vigorously when the key is turned to "start," yet the engines does not crank. This is a symptom of trouble in the starter drive.

Two types of starter drives are in common use. One, the Bendix drive system, is rapidly declining in popularity. In this system the starter drive pinion is forced into engagement with the flywheel ring gear by the inertia developed when the starter motor is activated. The second drive system is called the overrunning clutch type. It employs a solenoid to mechanically engage the drive pinion with the flywheel gear. Occasionally a starter drive will jam in the engaged position. On cars with manual transmissions it can usually be freed by selecting low gear and pushing the car slightly backward.

Careless engagement of the starter may result in a stripped flywheel gear. This is an expensive and complicated repair which must be left to a properly equipped shop. The starter usually makes a horrible jangling sound while turning the engine jerkily or not at all. Faulty solenoids and starter motors can sometimes be repaired, but one electrical failure may only be the start of many. In most cases it's best to obtain a new or rebuilt replacement for troublesome starting system components. Replacement armatures and windings are available for some units and may be installed separately should your tests locate the trouble in one of these assemblies.

Modern starting systems are not only a vast improvement over the hand crank, but a lot more reliable and powerful than their counterparts of a mere fifteen years ago. Given a bit of preventive maintenance around the battery, its cables and connections, today's starting system will normally supply faultless service for the life of the car.

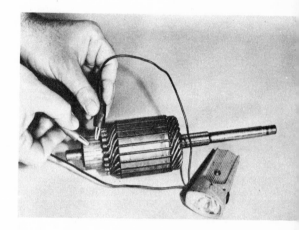

Loose windings sometimes occur when hard cranking melts solder on commutator. All commutator bars should have electrical contact with one another when tested.

Grounded starter field windings can be found by testing between the starter's main terminal and the frame. Make sure brushes don't touch frame during test.

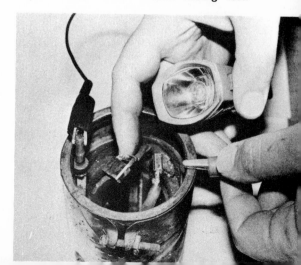

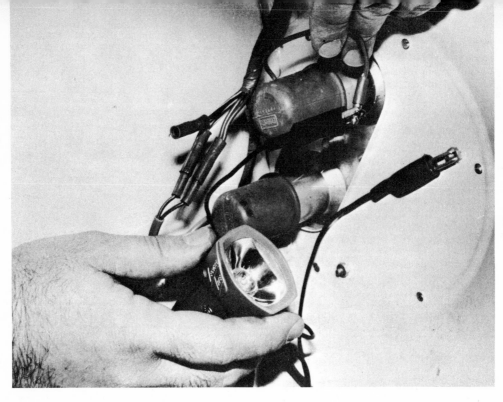

When a light stops burning and it isn't just a burned out bulb, you have to know how and where to find the trouble. Pull-apart connectors are a good place to start.

LIGHTS AND WIRING

Practical procedures for locating automotive electrical problems

Many car owners suspect they lack the competence required to work on their automobile's wiring and electrical accessories. Others fear they may receive a severe electrical shock. Actually, there's no danger and nothing so complicated that a sixth-grade science student couldn't figure it out.

Every driver should keep extra fuses, a roll of electrical tape, spare bulbs, a test light, and a couple of sealed beam headlight units in his car at all times. Most electrical failures occur suddenly while driving at night. You may be miles from any kind of help, so being prepared for such emergencies is your best defense against them.

FUSES AND CIRCUIT BREAKERS

Know where your car's fuse block is located and have at least one spare fuse for each amp rating used. Fuses contain a thin metal strip that's designed to melt like a showgirl's heart in a diamond salesman's hotel room if a predetermined electrical load is exceeded. Current flow is measured in amperes, each fuse being rated at so many "amps" capacity. If a short or an overloaded accessory causes a circuit's current drain to rise above the fuse's amp rating the fuse "blows," thereby switching off current to that circuit.

Many late model cars have all or part of their electrical wiring protected by au-

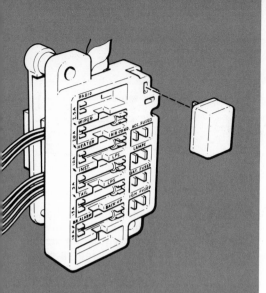

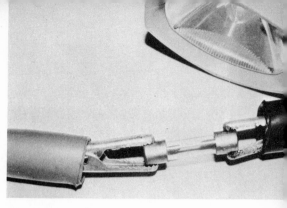

If the circuits of your car are protected by fuses, the fuse box is a good place to start checking for trouble. Know how to find burned out fuses, carry replacements.

Reading wiring diagrams can be a big help when trying to find electrical failures. These symbols are common: (A) ground, (B) battery, (C) switch, (D) coil (winding).

It's often a good idea to test fuses even if they do not appear to be burned out. A bump can sometimes break the fuse strips off the inside of one of the end pieces.

If you're sure that the fuses are alright check to see whether the light socket or electrical accessory is in solid contact electrically with the body of the car.

tomatic circuit breakers rather than by fuses. These devices cut off current briefly during overloads. A headlight short will cause the lights to go off and on repeatedly rather than leaving you without lights altogether as a fuse would.

Temporary overloads caused, for example, by windshield wipers that are bucking heavy snow can also blow fuses. In such cases it's only necessary to replace the fuse to return things to normal. But you definitely have trouble if you replace a fuse and the new one "blows" immediately. It's time to stop fussing with fuses and do some troubleshooting.

CIRCUITS

The negative (−) pole of the battery is usually connected to the body of the car. This is called *negative ground*. Until the early nineteen-fifties Ford products had the positive (+) pole of the battery grounded to the car's body, which now persists only on a few English cars.

Because one pole is grounded, an automotive electrical circuit normally consists of just one "hot" wire supplying positive (+) polarity to each light or accessory. Negative (−) polarity is obtained merely by placing the light or accessory in contact with the car's body.

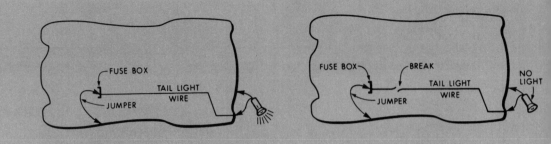

A battery-powered test light is a handy tool for tracing broken wiring since it doesn't rely on car's battery. It can be used in conjunction with a jumper as shown.

By removing a fuse and grounding the wire serving the circuit to be tested you can check it for breaks merely by connecting a test light to its other end and "ground."

WIRING DIAGRAMS

Because the return circuit takes place through the car's body it is possible to represent an automobile's electrical system with single lines indicating the "hot" wires. The owner's manuals for many foreign cars include wiring diagrams, but in most cases you'll need to obtain them from a shop manual for your particular automobile.

Wiring diagrams are *color coded*. That is, they indicate the various colors of wire used in different circuits. Headlight high-beams may be served by blue wires, low-beams by red and parking lights by black.

It is also possible to ground wires at their remote end and do your testing from the switch or the fuse box. Disconnect the car's battery while making such tests.

Other wires may have stripes of two different colors on their insulation. Color coding makes it possible to quickly locate the wire you are looking for on the car and to trace it from place to place even though it may be hidden from sight for part of its length.

SHORTS

A short circuit occurs whenever positive and negative conductors come into electrical contact in some way that is not intended. This could be only a wire with worn insulation that has sagged against the car's body or possibly two wires inside a motor that have broken down the insulation separating them. Shorts give electricity a "short cut" from negative to positive.

OPEN CIRCUITS

When an electrical path from negative to positive is incomplete it is called an open circuit. A broken wire or poor contact between an accessory and the car's body create unwanted open circuits. "Opens" do not blow fuses and the only way to pinpoint the trouble is to test the circuit thoroughly.

TROUBLESHOOTING

A test light that works on automobile current and another test light with its

own battery are almost indispensable for tracing automotive electrical ills. A jumper wire with small alligator clips on either end is also quite helpful. Study the diagrams showing how to test circuits with a test light carefully. Note how the jumper wire can be used to "ground" wires or accessories for testing.

When you are tracking down electrical troubles don't overlook switches and relays. Unless you are certain that current is reaching the switch and that the switch is delivering current when it is turned on there's no use in testing the lights, wiring, or accessories that it serves.

Trouble is frequently caused by rust or corrosion between a light bulb and its socket or between an accessory and the car's body. Poor ground contact is one of the first things to check. When your self-powered test light indicates that a bulb is alright, and your regular test light shows that current is reaching the light socket, you can be sure that rust is preventing the base of the bulb from achieving proper contact with "ground."

WIRE REPAIRS

Splice broken wires as shown in the photos. If your tests turn up a faulty wire that's encased in a harness along with a number of other wires it's best to string a separate wire to replace it. Auto supply stores have the correct type of wire as well as any terminals you may need.

Like shotguns, wire is made in various *gauges*. The smaller the number, the heavier the wire. Eight and ten-gauge are normally the largest and are used for primary connections between the generator and regulator and for "hot" wires leading to the fuse block and headlight switch. Twelve-gauge is used to serve current-hungry accessories such as starter solenoids and horn relays. Headlights may be wired with twelve or fourteen-gauge wire, the latter size also being used for radios, horns, heaters and most other accessories. Small lights usually get by with sixteen or eighteen-gauge wire.

Knowing how to troubleshoot wiring and electrical problems can do more than save the car owner the cost of many repairs. It's a matter of vital importance for coping with on-the-road emergencies.

To prepare a good wire splice, remove the insulation from both pieces and carefully intermix the individual strands. Next, twist the wire joint tightly together.

Heat the wire with a soldering iron and apply to small amount of solder. A resin core solder is best. If flux or acid core solder is used neutralize joint with soda.

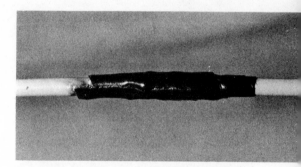

Wrap the joint with electrical tape after the solder has cooled. The adhesive may let loose with age, so it is usually best to cover the tape with a waterproof agent.

Liquid rubber is good for weatherproofing splices in wiring and preventing the tape from coming loose. Trim cement, Goodyear Pliobond and rubber cement work well also.

Regular cooling system tests may keep your radiator from freezing but they won't stop corrosion from attacking the metal parts and tired hoses of your engine from bursting.

KEEPING YOUR COOL

Proper care for the system that carries the lifeblood of your car

Overheating is the number-one all-time engine killer. Emission control devices and high performance engines have placed tremendous demands on cooling systems in recent years making their neglect something that no car owner can any longer afford.

COOLANTS

Most cars are designed to use an ethylene glycol type coolant in their radiators year round. These not only protect the cooling system against freezing but also against overheating since "permanent" antifreeze coolants have a higher boiling point than water. Most car makers recommend that a half water/half ethylene glycol mix be used both summer and winter. Many modern engines will actually boil if operated with only straight water in their cooling systems.

Obviously, "permanent" antifreeze is more than just "antifreeze." It is also far from being "permanent." The use of this word has probably led to more wrecked

Cars with aluminum blocks, heads, radiator cores or other cooling system parts need special consideration. Check to see that any products used are safe to use with aluminum.

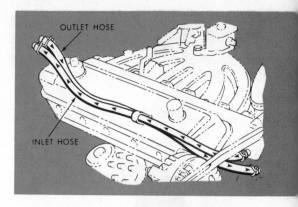

The heater hoses must usually be removed at the firewall to allow complete draining of the heater core. Inspect the heater hoses carefully for cracks, renew bad ones.

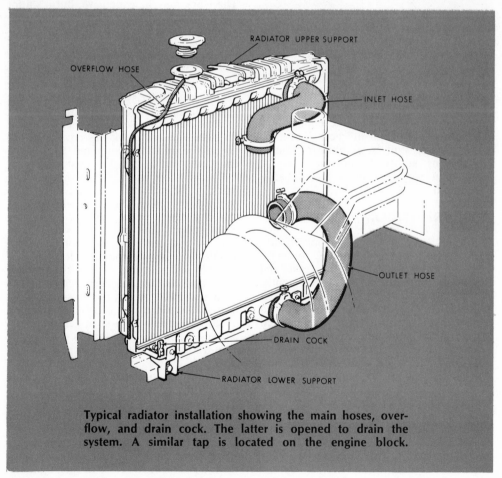

Typical radiator installation showing the main hoses, overflow, and drain cock. The latter is opened to drain the system. A similar tap is located on the engine block.

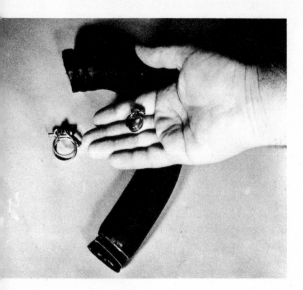

Hose clamps made from wire cut into the hose and cause early failure. For best hose life and easier removal replace them with clamps made from flat metal strips.

PLUGGED RADIATORS

When the build-up of rust and sludge becomes too severe radiator and heater core tubes may become totally plugged. Never refill a boiling cooling system from a creek or ditch since the addition of silt and organic matter is likely to add to the problem by further clogging the system. Adding water at a service station can be just as risky. The radiator filling bucket is often used to rinse windshield washing sponges as well. It's not unusual to find a collection of dead bugs and cigarette butts in the water they contain.

If your radiator is plugged badly enough to cause overheating it's too late for chemical cleaners. Take the car to a radiator shop that is equipped to disassemble radiators for mechanical cleaning. The work may be expensive, but it's a lot cheaper than a new engine. Annual flushing and fresh coolant are advised.

LEAKS

The addition of chemical leak sealers to neglected cooling systems can kill an engine quicker than a handful of sugar in the gas tank. Leaks that occur around hoses or where a crack has developed between the radiator core and one of its end tanks can be cured at least temporarily with "stop leak." However, pinhole leaks in the radiator tubes are there as a result of corrosion. Not only will the corrosion problem remain after the leak has been stopped, but unless steps are taken to clean and neutralize the cooling system additional leaks will soon develop.

Leak sealers can't distnguish between holes and coolant passages that have become narrowed by rust deposits—a condition that often exists in systems plagued by corrosion leaks. In such cases the addition of chemical leak sealers often result in a radiator so badly plugged with a cement-like residue that many radiator shops refuse to take the time to clean them. Putting leak sealer, or fresh antifreeze *containing* leak sealers, into a neglected cooling system can therefore end up costing as much as $120 for a new radiator. It's a lot cheaper to have the radiator cleaned and repaired professionally than to risk using a sealer in such systems.

cooling systems than forty Alaskan winters merely because car owers frequently interpret it to mean that the coolant will last forever. "Permanent" actually means only that the stuff is suitable for use in all seasons and does not need to be drained in Spring as older alcohol antifreezes did.

RUST PREVENTION

In addition to giving the coolant mixture a wide temperature range, "permanent" antifreeze also contains rust and corrosion inhibitors. After twelve months service these inhibitors are largely depleted. Within two years the coolant in your engine may have accumulated enough acids to actually *cause* corrosion.

Rusting cooling systems are always dangerous. Not only do rust deposits reduce the system's ability to dissipate heat, but loose particles accumulate to restrict the passage of coolant through heater and radiator core. Forget the word "permanent." Drain, flush, and refill the system with *new* coolant each year. It's one of the greatest favors you can do your engine.

ALUMINUM PARTS

Aluminum engines and radiators are easily destroyed by coolants and additives which are strongly alkaline. Some radiator cleaner preparations contain caustic compounds that can eat right through a light alloy engine block. Water with a high alkali content is also taboo. Before adding anything to a cooling system with aluminum parts make sure that the label on the can states that it is not harmful to this metal.

HOSES

Radiator and heater hoses should be given a careful inspection at each oil change. If they feel soft or spongy when squeezed they are overdue for replacement. Hoses that are hard and have cracks in them are likely to be brittle and should likewise be renewed. Heater hoses often burst with less provocation than radiator hoses. Make sure they are not wearing through at points where they may contact hot, vibrating engine parts. Bottom radiator hoses that have become soft may collapse while the engine is runnng and shut the flow of coolant off completely. Be particularly conscientious about checking this hose.

HOME REPAIRS

One doesn't have to be a mental giant to replace hoses or pour in new coolant. Nevertheless, there are a few tricks to the game. When draining the system remember to open the drain cock on the engine block as well as the one at the bottom of the radiator. Take off the radiator filler cap for a faster drain and never drain an engine while it is hot.

Heater cores seldom drain thoroughly unless the hoses are removed. Flush the heater by pressing a garden hose against the hoses serving it, allowing water to flow in both directions. Removing hoses so that the radiator and engine can be similarly rinsed out is also to be advised. Blowing through the heater core hoses will get the last bit of water out before replacing the hoses and installing new coolant.

When installing new hoses or replacing

What looks like coal dust plugging this radiator core is a cement-hard combination of rust and leak sealer. Never use sealer in a dirty system or use more than one can.

the old ones make certain that the tubes they go onto are clean. Rubbing the fittings with a bar of soap will help the hoses slip on easily and assume an even fit as the hose clamps are tightened. Hose clamps which consist of wire loops may cut into hoses and cause them to crack or leak. Clamps having flat metal bands are well worth the investment in terms of longer hose life and easier servicing.

SOLDERING

Radiator leaks frequently occur where the top or bottom tanks are soldered onto the core. Filling cracks and holes with solder is not difficult and is more durable and professional than leak sealer. In many cases the radiator need not be removed from the car, but on smaller automobiles even this is not a difficult job.

Drain the radiator and clean the area around the leak with fine emory cloth or steel wool until bright, bare metal shows. Brass or copper radiators should be soldered with a propane torch and solder having a *stearine* core. This type flows and seals best and presents fewer hazards to those with limited experience. Plumbers

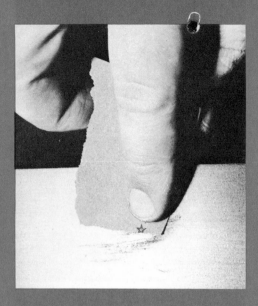

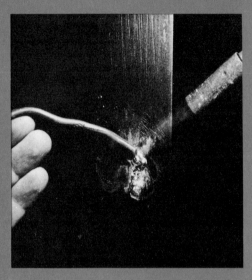

Leaking radiator tanks are easy to fix with solder. Drain the radiator and take it out of the car. Sand the area around the leak until bare, bright metal shows.

Heat the metal until it is hot enough to melt the solder. Allow the solder to flow over the leaking area. Repairs can be followed with a coat of radiator paint.

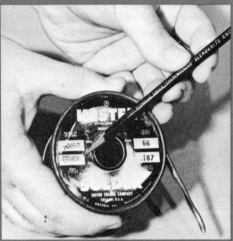

The best solder for home radiator repairs has a stearine core. This flux is non-corrosive and makes the soldering job a snap even for amateurs. Plumbers use it.

supply shops usually have it, but a good second choice is a paste-type soldering flux followed with plain 50/50 bar solder.

Special aluminum solder is available which can be used to repair aluminum radiators. It must be rubbed onto the bare metal with a large heated soldering iron. Once the aluminum has been coated with solder by rubbing, additional solder can easily be added to seal the leak. Plumber's supply departments and welders supply shops are the best source.

FILLER CAPS

Radiator caps have a pressure relief valve which must operate correctly to prevent overheating. Coolant under pressure boils at a higher temperature than the same coolant in an unpressurized system. Puzzling overheating problems can often be solved by having the cap tested for a weak spring or by putting the correct cap on a radiator which has had a lower pressure type installed by mistake.

Not all overheating problems are caused by cooling system trouble. Faulty emission controls such as spark advance overrides and stuck PCV valves can also give engines a fever.

THERMOSTATS

If the cooling system is being flushed it is wise to take off the thermostat housing that receives the top hose coming from the radiator. Clean the thermostat and check its operation by placing it in a pan of hot water along with a thermometer. The thermostat valve should stay completely closed until the water reaches the temperature at which the thermostat is rated. Older cars have 175° or 180° 'stats, but the newer jobs for smog control are usually rated at 195° or 200°. Many new cars will overheat if operated *without* a thermostat.

CORE PLUGS

So-called "freeze" plugs or core plugs are round metal discs pressed into openings in the side of the engine block. These may begin to eat through and leak if the cooling system has been neglected. Replacements are available. Just drill a hole in the old ones and pry them out. Clean openings and coat plugs with sealer before pounding them into place.

WATER PUMPS

When a water pump gets noisy or starts to leak there's nothing you can do but replace it. However, there are means of avoiding most such troubles. A can of water pump lube in the coolant won't hurt, and proper belt tensions are a "must." Over-tightened fan belts place an excessive strain on the pump shaft, as do poorly balanced fans.

GASKETS

Leaking cylinder head gaskets may allow hot gasses to enter the water jacket. This will produce overheating and rapidly increase the acidity of the coolant. Bubbles appearing in the top of the radiator with the engine hot and running are an easily checked clue. Cracked cylinder heads can cause similar troubles. They are usually the last stage before complete engine failure in cases where overheating has been severe. Needless to say, such trouble must be corrected immediately.

Hundreds of motorists take to the highways each summer with cooling systems that are in such poor condition that they quickly fail on high-speed superhighways. Taking care of the cooling system from the day the car is new can prevent such trouble. If neglect has already taken its toll it's better to pay the price of a radiator shop overhaul before leaving home than to suffer a wrecked engine and a ruined vacation later on.

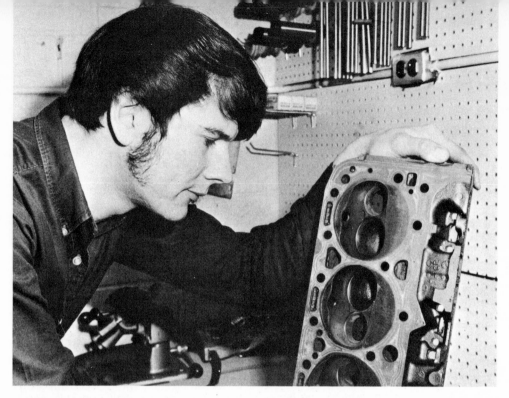

"Inspect it before you correct it" should be the watchword when doing a valve grind. Look for cracks, warpage, ruined seats in the head before you invest a lot of time, money.

VALVE GRINDS

The average car owner's first brush with advanced mechanical work

Sooner or later you're going to need a valve job no matter how well you take care of your car. Although great strides have been made in improving valve life since the early days of the automobile, the grueling conditions under which valves operate preclude any likelihood that a "lifetime" system will ever be developed. In recent years the valves' job has been made even more difficult by the legislation of various anti-pollution measures. Lean fuel/air mixtures reduce emissions while elevating valve temperatures. Lead-free gasoline denies valves the lubricating effect of former fuels. If present trends continue some experts believe that we may soon be doing valve grinds every 10,000 miles!

Valve grinds are expensive largely due to the labor involved in removing and replacing the cylinder heads. Even if this is the only part of the operation you choose to carry out yourself it can result in a very substantial saving. Actual valve work requires special tools, but it *is* possible to rent these at reasonable prices in most areas. It is also possible to "farm out" only part of the job, such as the actual grinding of the valves, then grind the seats and reinstall the valves yourself.

HEAD REMOVAL

The fewer cylinders your car has, the easier it is to do a valve job. V-8 engines are about twice as tough as an inline "six," and owners of four-cylinder

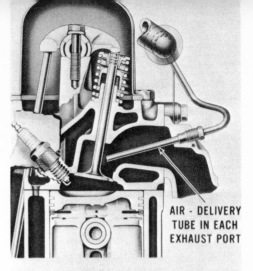

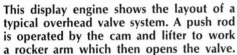

AIR - DELIVERY
TUBE IN EACH
EXHAUST PORT

This display engine shows the layout of a typical overhead valve system. A push rod is operated by the cam and lifter to work a rocker arm which then opens the valve.

When removing head from engines with air injection pollution control be careful not to damage the air delivery tubes. Pull the manifold up and out until tubes are clear.

cars should consider themselves lucky indeed. Not only are there fewer and generally less expensive valves to grind or replace on small "fours," but the small physical dimensions make it a snap to lift off and replace their cylinder heads.

Drain the water from the engine block and remove the valve cover(s). Never remove the heads while the engine is hot since it may cause them to warp. Take off the rocker arm assemblies if they interfere with reaching the cylinder head bolts. Unbolt the intake and exhaust manifolds. On V-8 engines you'll have to disconnect all the plumbing and linkages going to the intake manifold and carburetor, then lift off the entire manifold assembly. You may have trouble reaching the bolts holding the exhaust manifolds.

On inline engine's it's usually possible to unbolt the manifolds and merely pull them away from the head, leaving most of the plumbing and linkages attached. The exhaust pipe will usually provide adequate support for the manifolds on most

An electric drill and a stiff wire brush can be used to clean the carbon from cast iron heads, but not from aluminum. For the soft metal use a solvent and a plastic scraper.

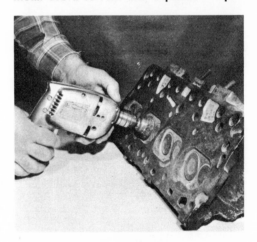

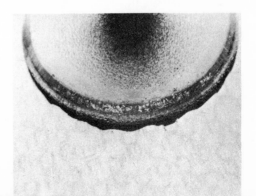

Although reuseable, this valve is ready for a grind. Pitting in valve facing allows it to leak slightly and cause the engine to lose compression, power, performance.

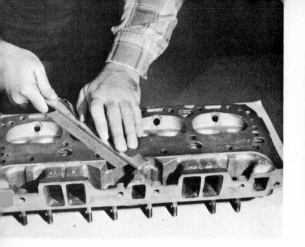

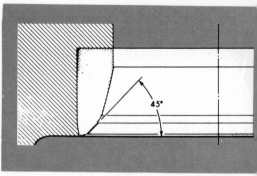

Clean the flat surfaces of the heads with fine-grit emery cloth wrapped over a flat piece of steel. This will remove bits of the old gaskets, sealer, and other debris.

Grind the valve seats to the proper angle using a freshly dressed stone or a reamer designed for the job. You may wish to let an automotive machine shop handle this.

domestic inline engines, but on imports the intake manifold may be separate and have to be supported by a length of wire. Volkswagen engines must be removed from the car before the heads can be taken off.

Once everything has been unbolted from the cylinder heads you may begin loosening the cylinder head bolts. Make sure that you get them all, including those in the center of the head. Loosen them until the bolt heads are about ⅛" clear of the engine. Run the starter briefly so that engine compression breaks the seal between the head and the block, then remove the spark plugs. Take out the head bolts and lift the cylinder head(s) off the engine.

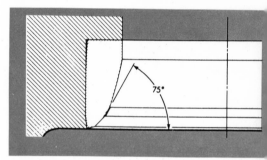

A seventy-five degree reamer or stone can be used to raise the seat and to narrow it to the width recommended by the car maker. This is often skipped in repair shops.

GRINDING

Once the head is off there are several courses of action open to you. One of these is to deliver the cylinder head to a machine shop which can handle all phases of the valve grinding work. Such facilities are listed under "Automobile Machine Shop Services" in the yellow pages of your telephone directory. This is a wise choice if valve guides need replacing since they have the special tools required for pulling the old ones and pressing in on the new. The cost of the

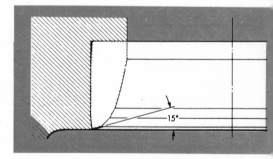

The seats are narrowed from above with the help of a fifteen-degree cutter or stone. Seat widths that are within specfications guarantee the longest possible valve life.

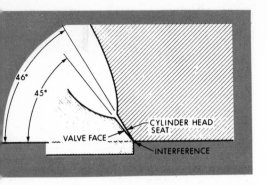

It's common to grind a slight interferance between the valve and the seat. Car makers sometimes specify 46° seats and 45° valves or 45° seats and 44° valves. Check specs.

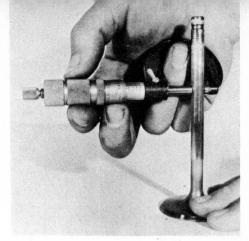

There's no use grinding a valve when its stem is galled or worn. A worn stem will not fit even when new guides are installed. Replace when mike shows undersize.

A special machine is required for refacing engine valves. Sometimes this tool can be rented, but on 4-cylinder engines the cost can almost equal a new set of valves!

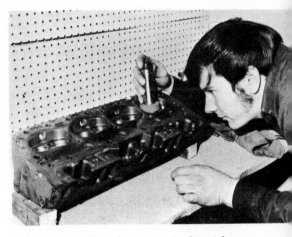

Make certain that the stone is dressed at the correct angle and that its pilot fits the guide. Rented grinding tools sometime need considerable attention before using.

work will probably be from $15 to $25 per head, but they'll be ready to install when you get them back. The alternative is to do as much of your own work as possible.

PREPARATION

Cleaning cylinder head and valves is the first step if you elect to grind the valve yourself. A wire brush chucked in a power drill can be used to scour carbon from combustion chambers in cast iron heads. Aluminum heads, however, should be cleaned with a wood or plastic scraper and carburetor cleaning solvent. This is especially important when cleaning old bits of gasket and sealer from the face of the head since even tiny gouges in the light alloy can produce leaks when

Don't remove any more metal from the seats than is necessary to remove pitting. The weight of the grinder should be supported so stone is not pressed too hard.

the new gasket is installed. Be careful on cast iron too, using solvent to soften carbon and sealer rather than relying on heavy pressure and a wire brush.

The next step is to take out the valves. You'll need a valve spring compressor for this job. Keep the valves, springs and keepers in order so you'll be able to return them to the same cylinders they came from. If there are heavy carbon accumulations inside the cylinder head ports these must be removed too, but be careful not to damage the valve seats. The valves will also have carbon deposits on them which must be knocked off with a power driven wire brush mounted on your bench grinder.

CUTTING SEATS

The valve seats in the cylinder head can be resurfaced with a special power

grinder or with a hand reamer. Seat grinding sets are often available from tool rental companies, but make sure that the stones are dressed to the proper angle before attacking your head.

Hand-operated valve reseating reamers cost between $5 and $20 depending on the set. The least expensive contain only a 45° cutter for resurfacing the seat itself. The best, however, include 60° and 30° cutters for bringing the seat back to its proper width after the surface has been cut to 45°. Narrowing the seats to specifications can be beneficial both to valve life and performance, but it's a step that's skipped even in many machine shops. Exhaust seats should usually be .090″ to .100″ wide and intakes .070″ to .090″, but the manufacturer's specs for your car should be taken as the final authority.

Do not exert heavy pressure when cutting seats with a power grinder. Even the weight of the motor is too much, so support it lightly while making the cut. A coarse stone is used for the first cut to remove pitting and roughness. This is followed by a fine stone which provides the final "polish." For a smooth grind, lift the stone occasionally while making the cut and don't allow the motor to bog down.

Hand reamers should be lubricated when used to cut valve seats. A mixture of kerosene and motor oil works well. Take time to clean the metal chips from the cutters repeatedly during each cut and use only very light pressure. Let the tool do the work, not your strong right arm. Abrasive type reseating tools are also available which are good for giving the seat a final finish.

GUIDES

Some modern engines have no valve guides. In such cases wear must be accommodated by using new valves with oversize stems. It's important that the valve guides be in good condition before cutting the seats so that the stone or cutter will run true. While it is possible to hammer out removable guides using a drift or bushing driving tool, it's also very crude. Driving new guides in with a hammer rather than using a press is likewise not in the interest of best results. Guide replacement is one job that it's nearly always best to "farm out" to a machine shop. Tools are available for scrubbing varnish and carbon from the inside of used guides, but a rifle bore brush and carb cleaner will usually do the trick.

VALVE REFACING

Unless you are installing new valves you'll have to obtain the use of a refacing grinder. You may be able to rent one, but since most automotive machine shops will grind your old valves for about 25¢ apiece it's hardly worth the expense. If you do your own refacing note especially whether the widest edge of the valve head retains an adequate margin. If it comes to a knife edge by the time all pitting has been ground from the valve face you'll have to throw it away and obtain a new valve. If the margin is of irregular width it shows that the valve is warped and must likewise be replaced. Valves with obvious damage or with stems which prove to be undersize when measured with a micrometer should also be rejected.

It is normal practice today to grind the valves at a somewhat shallower angle than the seats to produce a slight "wedge" fit. Usually the valve faces are ground to a true 44°. Make certain that the stone on the refacing machine is dressed properly to produce a true flat cut.

LAPPING

Lapping the valves into their individual seats with abrasive valve grinding compound is a relatively rare practice these days. An interference fit between a 45° seat and a 44° valve face is considered adequate for reliable sealing. Nevertheless, lapping still has its place. Many mechanics have found that lightly lapping each valve after machine grinding can add considerably to valve life. If the seats are in very good condition it is also possible to have the valves refaced and then lapped in until the seats are completely smooth without any mechanical resurfacing or cutting of the seats.

If you are going to lap the valves in with grinding compound it's very important that they be installed in their own seat. Mark them with waterproof ink to make certain.

Fine water-based grinding compound is best for most purposes. Apply a very small amount to the valve face and drop it into the seat. A crank-operated valve grinding tool can be used to grip and turn the valve or it can be done with a common suction cup on the end of a wooden handle. Rotate the valve about a third of a turn at a time, lifting it free of the seat after each movement. Continue until a smooth band shows completely around the valve and valve seat. Make certain that all abrasive is cleaned from the valve and cylinder head after you have finished.

REASSEMBLY

Valves should always be returned to their original seats. Inspect the keepers and retainers for wear and replace any that are damaged. If the springs are progressively wound, place the end of the spring which has its coils closest together

This step isn't so important on older cars that are never driven hard, but if you are going racing or own a high-revving import always have valve spring tensions checked.

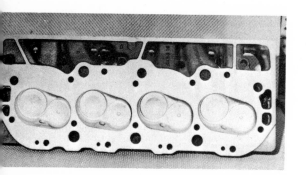

Here's what a finished head should look like. Everything is clean and ready for installation. All carbon has been removed and head facing is now smooth and true.

When replacing the cylinder head check the push rods to see that none are bent. Roll them on a flat table or a piece of glass. This will locate any that are not straight.

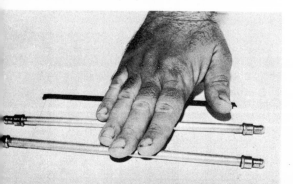

next to the cylinder head. If your engine is frequently operated at high speeds, as in drag racing, it's important to have springs tested for proper tension. Service is available at most machine shops.

Lubricate the valve stems before putting them into the head. Most engines have rubber-like valve seals which slip over the valve stems and the tops of the guides. These are to prevent oil from being sucked through the guides and should always be replaced with new ones at each valve grind. Install the springs and compress them so retainers can be slipped onto the valve stems.

ENGINE CLEANING

While the cylinder head is at the machine shop or lying on your work bench the tops of the pistons and cylinder block should be cleaned. Solvent and a putty knife are traditional tools, but a plastic scraper is best for aluminum pistons. A power-driven wire brush can also be used to clean up cast iron blocks if all water and bolt holes are first covered with bits of masking tape to keep the dust out. The engine can be turned to bring each piston to the top for cleaning and the remaining cylinders plugged with rags to prevent dirt from entering.

HEAD GASKETS

There are two types of gaskets commonly used on today's engines. One is a sandwich-like assembly consisting of two soft metal sheets bonded together over an asbestos-rubber compound. The other is a thin metal sheet having a multitude of ridges embossed into it. The latter type is pre-coated with an aluminum sealing compound and should not be treated with additional sealer. They should only be used with head and block surfaces that are in good condition.

Composition head gaskets have a "top" side, which is usually marked. Some car makers specify that sealer be applied to one or both sides of these gaskets before installing them. If no sealer is required, lubricate them lightly with vaseline so that they will squeeze out smoothly as the head is bolted down. *Never reuse a head gasket.*

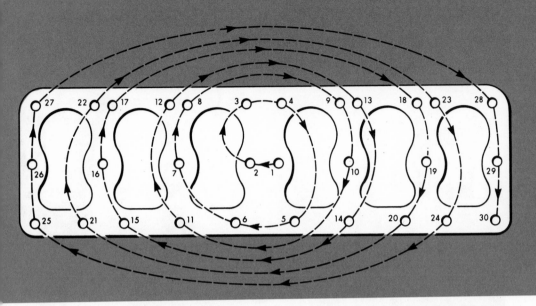

If you have a shop manual it will give the order for torquing the head bolts. This chart shows the basic pattern that is used on all engines. Always start your work at center.

HEAD REPLACEMENT

Lower the head carefully onto the new gasket so that all bolt holes align perfectly. Coat the threads of the head bolts with oil and screw them in lightly. When all are in place, begin tightening them with a torque wrench.

Start torquing the head in the middle so that the gasket is squeezed out smoothly in both directions. If the torque specifications are 75 foot pounds tighten them only about 25 foot pounds, then go over the bolt pattern again bringing them to 50 foot pounds. Make a third pass at the full 75 foot pounds and give those in the center a final check to see that they are still within specifications. A service manual for your car will give the bolt tightening sequence but if this is unavailable work outward in spirals from the center as shown on the chart.

FINAL TOUCHES

Roll the push rods on a smooth table before putting them back into the engine. This will help detect any that may be bent. Torque the manifold bolts to the car maker's specifications using new gaskets. If the engine has hydraulic lifters, adjust the valves according to the procedure given in the shop manual for your car. If not, adjust the valves as described in the chapter on tune-ups allowing about .002″ wider settings than normal. They should not be adjusted to their normal lash until after at least 100 miles of driving.

One final word of advice: *Keep everything clean.* The cleaner the job, the better it will be. Professional speed tuners work in an almost "hospital" atmosphere when grinding valves. A good job is vital to them, as it should be to you when working on your own car. If you decide to "farm out" your valve grind work, don't overlook speed shop services. Their machinist may charge $10 or $25 more for a valve grind than "repair" shops do, but the quality of the work is so superior as to almost defy description.

An engine overhaul usually consists of a valve grind plus new rings and bearings. It may be necessary, however, to have some of the engine's major components reconditioned also.

ENGINE OVERHAULS

It requires time and precision tools to rebuild your car's engine

Valve grinds are often done without touching the rest of the engine, but overhauling an engine without also doing a valve grind is like vacationing in Paris and never leaving your hotel room. Once the cylinder head is off it takes very little additional work to put the valves back in shape. However, determining when an engine needs more than a simple valve job takes a bit of doing.

SYMPTOMS

It's never wise to settle for just a valve job on high-mileage engines. Unless the pistons and rings are in good shape a valve grind may lead to excessive oil consumption. Also, should a compression check reveal that one or two cylinders are below par, don't jump to the conclusion that a simple valve job will cure the condition. You can determine whether piston rings or valves are causing the compression drop by squirting a quantity of motor oil into the affected cylinders and repeating the compression test. If the reading improves significantly the trouble is piston rings. When adjacent cylinders show low compression readings, there may be a leak in the head gasket between them.

A trail of bluish smoke from the exhaust pipe during deceleration is a traditional sign that a ring job is needed. When light smoke and vapor pour from the oil filler when the cap is removed from an idling engine it also indicates that the rings are not doing their job, especially if it's accompanied by a sharp puff of air as each cylinder fires. Falling oil pressure and knocking sounds mean bearing troubles. A rattling knock usually indicates worn connecting rod bearings. A heavy throbbing thump during acceleration or as the engine is started points to main bearings.

DO IT YOURSELF

Once you've determined that your engine needs an overhaul you'll have to consider that doing the job yourself requires a considerable investment in time and talent. First, the engine must be removed, a job which varies from car to car in complexity. After the engine is out and disassembled the various parts must be measured with micrometers to determine whether oversize pistons and bearings will be needed to correct wear and whether the block, pistons, or connecting rods will require machine shop reconditioning. Until this is done it's impossible to buy the correct replacement parts. You'll also have to obtain a shop manual to get accurate clearance specifications for your engine. Unless you are prepared to do without a car for a week or more and to devote every moment of your spare time to its repair you'd be well advised to turn the job over to a professional shop.

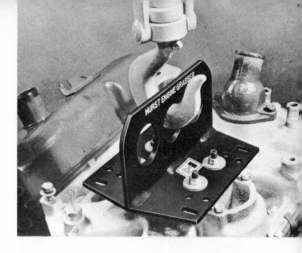

For an overhaul the engine must come out of the car. This means that you'll need the proper tools for lifting it. Don't take a chance dropping it with makeshift methods.

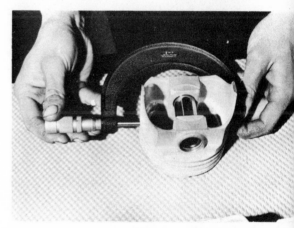

There is little use in doing a "ring job" if the pistons themselves are undersize. Even new pistons should be miked with care to obtain a perfect fit with the cylinder.

The cylinder bores should be checked for wear and to determine piston clearance. A dial indicator gauge such as this is quick and accurate but snap gauges will work too.

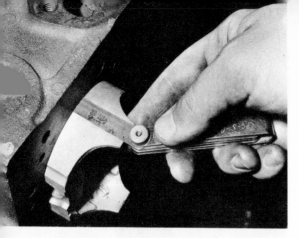

Although not so accurate as miking the cylinder and piston, piston clearance can be checked by inserting a piston in the bore and measuring with a feeler gauge.

Cylinders which are worn too badly must be rebored to accept new and larger pistons. A machine such as this which is fitted to the cylinder block is used to do the work.

Even if the cylinder does not need to be rebored there will be a top cylinder ridge like this. It must be removed before new rings are installed to avoid breaking them.

This tool is called a ridge reamer and it is used to remove top cylinder ridges when new rings are installed. One suitable for home use costs between about $8 and $10.

PISTON FIT

Piston ring replacement is a rather common job and requires less time and effort than a complete overhaul. However, it is useless to replace piston rings if the pistons and cylinders themselves show considerable wear. Inferior rings are sometimes used in new cars which quickly wear out. In such cases replacing them with premium quality parts will do

the trick. In high mileage engines, however, the cylinder bores should be measured and the pistons carefully inspected to determine whether they can be reused.

Check the cylinder walls for taper. Generally speaking, if the lower part of a cylinder is no more than .005″ larger than its top it is not excessively tapered. A shop manual will list the exact wear limit for your car. The cylinders must also be checked for out-of-round. Usually, a cylinder which measures within .002″ front to rear of its side to side dimension is acceptable for reuse.

If a cylinder fails to meet the standards for taper and out-of-round the block will have to be bored to accept an oversize piston. If performance happens to be your bag it's best to replace all the pistons with the same oversize. Such work requires the services of a machine shop and they'll need to have the new pistons on hand so that the cylinders may be bored accurately to size.

A very slight taper can sometimes be corrected or brought within approved tolerances by honing. A hone can also be used to erase minor scratches, light scoring, and metallic deposits caused by scuffing pistons. However, such easily corrected wear will usually be found only in engines which are below the 50,000 mile mark.

There is also a limit to how much honing can be done without affecting piston fit. The rule of thumb is to allow .001″ of clearance between an aluminum piston and its cylinder for each inch of bore diameter. This means that a 4-inch piston should have about .0035″ to .004″ of clearance. A shop manual will provide more explicit specifications for your engine, however.

Piston clearance is determined by placing the piston in the bore and inserting a long feeler gauge between it and the cylinder wall. If the old pistons are too loose it is imperative that new ones

be obtained which can correct the wear. If the block is rebored to accept oversize pistons the final honing should be checked frequently by measuring piston clearance until a perfect fit is obtained.

OVERSIZE PISTONS

New pistons are available in a number of oversizes. These require that the cylinders be rebored to accept them. However, most car makers have also established high and low tolerance limits for "standard" piston size and this can be taken advantage of when cylinders are only lightly worn. For example, should the cylinders show about .0015″ wear it can easily be accommodated by using "standard" pistons from the high end of the tolerance scale. The parts man at your car dealer's service department will be able to fill you in on what's available. This trick may save the expense of an overbore for .010″ pistons which are usually the first oversize available. Some foreign car makers offer oversize pistons only .0025″ above standard size which can also provide a way out.

PISTON CONDITION

Pistons must also be checked for wear and distortion of their skirts. If the top ring groove has widened the piston can be reconditioned by a machine shop to accept a spacer in addition to the normal ring. If the lower ring grooves are worn

After cylinders have been bored or the top ridge removed they should be honed to remove "glaze" and aid ring seating. The hone is moved vertically for crosshatch.

It is important that pistons be returned to their original cylinders. They can be marked with waterproof ink, a center-punch, or with a number stamping set.

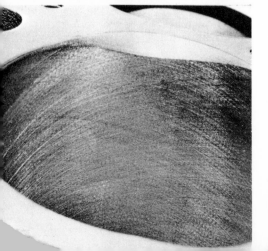

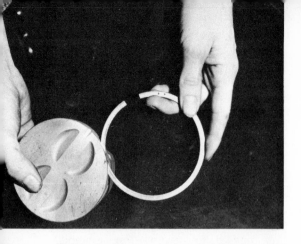 

Check the pistons to see that the grooves haven't collapsed. Roll new ring in the piston to check for tight spots. Rings must be able to rotate freely on the pistons.

If clearance between the ring and piston grooves is too small the rings will seize as the engine heats up. Top ring should have .002", and others a .0015" clearance.

excessively a new piston is needed.

Pistons which are not badly worn, but which have "collapsed skirts" will rock in their bores and ruin the new rings. If the damage isn't excessive the pistons can be restored by knurling. This involves having grooves or a waffle pattern pressed into their skirt. Most automotive machine shops will do the work at low cost.

If the wrist pin bores are worn it is possible to fit oversize wrist pins on many engines. This job requires a special honing machine and is best farmed out to a machine shop. Most dealer's service departments take advantage of these same outside services.

RING FIT

Oversize pistons require oversize rings. It's often cheaper to buy them pre-assembled. If you are going to install the rings yourself it's important to check their fit with the pistons and with the cylinder bores. End clearance is exceedingly important since too little will cause the ring to seize in the cylinder and too much may cause leakage. Insert the rings one by one into the cylinder bores and check the gap with a feeler gauge. They should also be rolled edgeways in the piston grooves and the side clearance measured with a feeler gauge. Specifi-

cations for ring fit are given in the shop manual for your car, however an end gap of .001" per inch of cylinder bore is a popular rule of thumb. A special tool is available for expanding rings so that they can be slipped onto the pistons easily. It's a good investment in most cases, although the rings for small cars can often be spread and slipped on by hand. You'll definitely need a piston ring compressor to hold the rings in their grooves while the pistons are being inserted into the block.

PISTON INSTALLATION

There is usually a ridge of metal left around the top of used cylinder bores. This is produced by the wearing away of that portion of the cylinder contacted by the piston rings. Unless this top ridge is removed it may cause the new piston rings to break. There's a tool called a ridge reamer which should be used to remove this.

While slower, it is also possible to remove top cylinder ridges with emory cloth over a semicircular block of wood. A fine abrasive stone chucked in an electric drill can be used to remove the bulk of the ridge if you are steady handed and careful not to scratch the cylinder wall below the ridge. Follow this with emory cloth for a smooth finish.

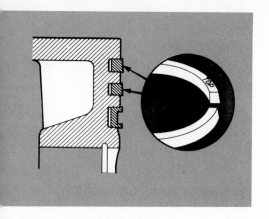

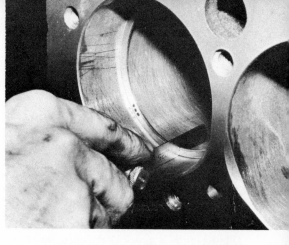

Piston rings are not perfectly rectangular in cross section. Getting them right side up is important. Look for the word "TOP" or for two dots on the top of each ring.

Check piston ring end clearance by placing the ring in the cylinder and measuring the gap with a feeler gauge. Allow about .001" for each inch of the cylinder bore diameter.

The cylinders should also be honed lightly to break the "glaze" on their surfaces. This will help the cylinder walls to retain lubrication and aid the new rings in seating. Raise and lower the hone in the yclinder bore as it rotates to produce a cross-hatch pattern. Do not hone any longer than is necessary to produce an even pattern over the cylinder walls. Use fine abrasives if soft iron rings are to be used, coarser abrasives when chrome rings are installed.

Lubricate the pistons and rings, clamp on the ring compressor, and insert the connecting rod and piston skirt into the cylinder. Tap the top of the piston lightly with a hammer handle to push the rings down into the cylinder. It is wise to slip two short lengths of rubber hose over the connecting rod bolts to prevent their threads accidently damaging the crankshaft journals. Guide the rod end onto the crankshaft and install the rod cap and nuts. Torque the rods to specifications and don't forget to use new lock nuts. Reusing the old ones or leaving them out altogether has put a sudden end to many recently overhauled engines.

Fitting piston pins both to the pistons and to the connecting rods requires special tools such as this which are accurate to a ten-thousandth of an inch. Farm this job out.

THE CRANKSHAFT

Unless there has been a cataclysmic bearing or lubrication failure you'll sel-

dom need to replace a crankshaft. Wear, however, may make it necessary to recondition the shaft. Measure each main and rod bearing journal with a micrometer. Check both sides of each journal, making two measurements at 90° to one another at each point. If there's a differ-

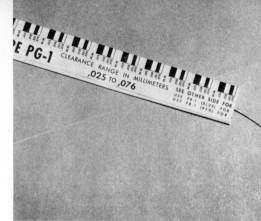

Plastigage is a quick and cheap means of checking bearing clearances. It can tell old bearing clearance (.002" shown here), can also be used when fitting new bearings.

Plastigage is a plastic string which comes in a paper envelope bearing a number of scales for measuring the clearance shown by the flattened strip of plastic material.

It is alright to place plastigage near the oil holes, but be careful that it is not positioned so that it crosses an oil hole in either the crank journal or connecting rod.

The bearing shells have a small lug at one end to lock them in place in the bearing caps or saddles. Check to see that this matches the notch cut into the engine part.

ence of more than .002" between any of these readings the crank will have to be turned over to a machine shop for reconditioning.

If the wear is fairly uniform, but the diameter of the journals has worn down by .001" or .002", it is possible to obtain new bearings which will compensate for this condition. It is rare, however, that bearings of more than .001" oversize can be fitted without regrinding crankshaft.

When a crankshaft is reconditioned by grinding all journals are usually taken down to a common undersize to match the oversize bearing sets available. This is usually .010", .020" or .030". Obviously one should not obtain new bearings until the crankshaft has been miked and reconditioned if necessary. If the engine has main bearing trouble, check crankshaft for straightness even though the journals may be within wear tolerances.

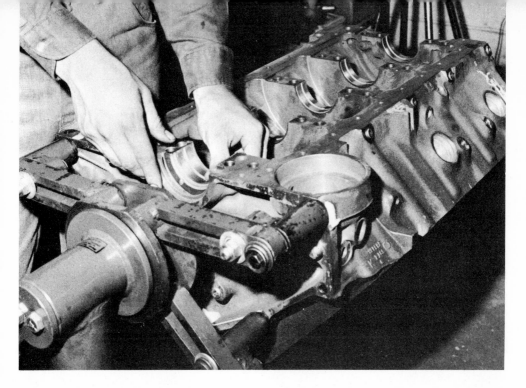

Make absolutely certain that there is no accumulation of dirt in the bearing saddles or caps as the new bearing shells are installed. All parts must be kept clean in final assembly.

Never install a reconditioned crank until you have cleaned it thoroughly *yourself*. Scrub out the oil passages using solvent and a rifle bore brush, then blow them out with compressed air or swab them clean with cloth patches or pipe cleaners. Abrasives and metal particles left from the grinding operation could destroy the shaft and new bearings during the first few minutes of operation.

BEARINGS

Even though you're positive that the parts man has given you the correct bearing set for your engine, check them anyway. Make sure that the oil holes are in the correct location to match those in the mainbearing webs. Also check to see that the oil grooves are identical to those of the original bearings. If not, their wear pattern will be different from that of the used crankshafft. Reject any which show obvious physical damage.

When installing the bearing shells be certain that the locating lugs stamped into them properly engage the corresponding slots in the housings. The bearings will be slightly greater than 180° and you'll notice that the ends of each shell stick up fractionally above the bearing caps or saddles. Don't file them down. The feature is intentional and designed to give just the correct degree of "crush" required to seat the bearings properly.

BEARING FIT

A trial fitting of the new bearings should always be made before final assembly. At this time actual working clearances between the crankshaft journals and the bearing shells can be measured with Plastigage. Plastigage kits can be obtained from any auto parts jobber. They consist of a length of soft plastic rod and a simple measuring scale.

On high performance engines the main bearing caps should first be installed without bearing shells and the main bearing bores checked for roundness. If a block has enough cylinder wear to require re-

93

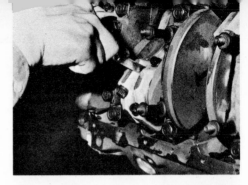

The crank journals and bearing shells must be pre-lubricated as they are assembled. If not they could be ruined the moment the engine is started due to a lack of oil.

It's important to check rod bearing side-clearance on V-8 engines. This is done with a feeler gauge. .008″ to .015″ is approximately right for most stock powerplants.

boring a similar check should be made prior to delivering it to the machine shop so that the bearing housings can be align-bored at the same time. Actually, the home mechanic who intends to farm out everything except disassembly and reassembly can rely on the machinist to check all required measurements.

If the bearing bores are true, make certain that everything is completely clean and free of lubrication, then fit the main bearing shells into their housings. Lower the crankshaft carefully onto the up-ended block. Lay a strip of Plastigage across the journal just slightly off center so that it will not be in line with the oil hole in the bearing cap. Install the bearing cap and torque the bolts to specifications.

The Plastigage will be flattened out as the bearing cap is bolted down. Remove the bearing cap and measure the width of the Plastigage strip with the scale provided. This will show the actual working clearance of the bearing. A similar process is followed when checking connecting rod bearings. Plastigage can actually substitute for a micrometer in low milage engines. The car maker's specifications as to proper clearance should always be adhered to, but main bearing clearances generally fall into the .0015″ to .0025″ range with rod bearing clearances slightly wider at .002″ to .003″.

Needless to say, everything should be spotlessly clean during final assembly. Also, the bearings should be pre-lubricated with a special preparation for this purpose or with a product such as STP Oil

Treatment or General Motors Engine Oil Supplement. This will keep the new bearings from being ruined before engine oil begins to circulate on the first test run.

CONNECTING RODS

The con rods on most low-output engines will last forever with no attention. High performance models, however, can be very hard on their rods and these should always be taken to a machine shop for a thorough check and possible reconditioning. Actually, it's not a bad idea on any engine. The rods should be checked for alignment, concentric big ends, and stretching. If a rod cannot be reconditioned it is often possible to buy a reconditioned replacement which costs considerably less than a new rod.

If new pistons are being installed in the engine the wrist pins must be accurately fitted to the connecting rods. Most cars have removable bushings in the rods' small end. New bushings can be pressed in with an ordinary vise to correct wear and match the rod to standard-diameter wrist pins. However, the bushing must also be reamed or honed to the proper clearance. While hand reamers are available, the whole operation of piston pin fitting is best left to a professional machine shop.

Correct pin fit in both the piston and connecting rod can be measured in ten-thousandths of an inch. If there's any noticeable rocking play at this point with the pin lubricated it almost certainly means

Check the valve lifter bores with a snap-type rod gauge. If they are worn oversize lifters should be obtained to correct the wear. Check the lifter diameters as well.

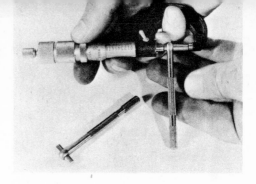

Once locked, the snap gauge can be checked with a micrometer. Cylinder bores, main bearing and connecting rod bores, and cam bearing bores can also be checked.

that wear is excessive. Checking manufacturer's specifications is vital and obtaining best possible fit requires highly specialized machining and measuring tools.

CAM AND LIFTERS

One worn cam lobe can knock dozens of horses off the team in a high-performance engine. Obvious wear is always reason enough to obtain a reconditioned camshaft. Use new cam bearings and be careful when inserting the camshaft so that the lobes do not scratch the bearing shells. Plenty of pre-assembly lube should be applied to both the cam bearings and lobes since these parts are under great stress from the moment the engine starts.

If the valve lifter bores have worn to a clearance greater than about .005″ new lifters should be obtained. These are often available in oversizes to correct for wear.

ASSEMBLY

It is not intended that this chapter provide step-by-step instructions for an engine overhaul. Rather, we have discussed techniques required to accomplish the specific tasks included in engine rebuilding. A shop manual should always be considered the last word on how to take things apart and put them together and what specifications need to be met in the fitting of new parts.

When assembling an engine after extensive rebuilding, care must be taken to exclude all dirt and other foreign matter.

If lifter bores are worn tapered or badly galled they can be honed oversize with a brake cylinder hone. Oversize lifters can then be used to correct for the increase.

Adhere strictly to bolt torque specifications at all times. Use new gaskets and install them on clean, dry surfaces. Obtain a good grade of gasket cement for use on cork gaskets and wherever else required. Unless all gaskets and seals are fitted carefully you will have oil and coolant leaks to contend with which may only be curable by disassembling the engine and replacing the gaskets.

While it's true that a certain amount of mechanical know-how is prequisite to attempting an engine overhaul, tyro mechanics should nevertheless be able to save money on such work providing they take their time and farm out any jobs they are not able to handle.

Drag racers expect to tear up a clutch or transmission occasionally, it's part of the game. If you make drag racing starts you can expect much of the same from your car.

PROJECT SMOOTH SHIFT

Many common clutch and transmission troubles can be cured at home

Some drivers never experience clutch or transmission failures. These lucky individuals do not speed shift, peel rubber, make jackrabbit starts or downshift to slow their cars instead of using the brakes. But neglecting the "little" things that constitute routine maintenance can cause their share of trouble too.

SLIPPING CLUTCHES

Even cars that are never abused may develop a slipping clutch. Usually it shows up first during hard acceleration. The engine gains speed rapidly but the car fails to go significantly faster. Inadequate freeplay is the usual problem. Normally, the clutch pedal should go down easily for about ¾" before it meets with solid resistance. The freeplay decreases as the clutch facings wear and periodic adjustments are required to keep it within acceptable limits.

ADJUSTING FREEPLAY

Freeplay adjustments are made under the car on the left side of the engine's flywheel bellhousing. The clutch throwout arm projects from the bellhousing at this point and moves back and forth as the clutch pedal is operated. A threaded rod engages the outer end of the throwout arm. This is fitted with an adjusting nut and a locknut so that alterations can be made to the rod's working length. To adjust clutch pedal freeplay loosen the locknut and turn the adjusting nut until the

These are the clutch components: pressure plate assembly, driven disc and flywheel. This is a special Schiefer unit designed especially for hard use at the drag strip.

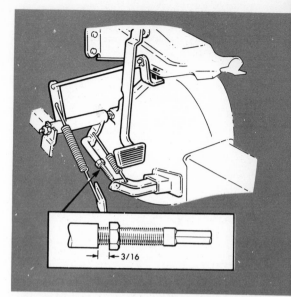

Adjusting clutch freeplay is an important phase of car maintenance. Adjustment is under car on left side of bellhousing. A 3/4" free pedal movement is about right.

clutch pedal moves about 3/4" before beginning to operate the clutch throwout arm, then re-tighten the locknut. This dimension may vary slightly with the make and model car.

Freeplay can be adjusted on cars with hydraulic clutches without reference to the pedal. Remove the spring from the throwout arm and turn the adjustment until the hydraulic piston has 1/10" of free travel. On VWs and most other rear-engined cars the adjustment is located on a threaded rod attached to the rear of the clutch cable. If adjusting freeplay does not cure the slippage there's throuble within the clutch itself.

DRAGGING CLUTCH

Excessive freeplay will prevent the clutch from disengaging fully. A dragging clutch causes clashing gear changes no matter how carefully you try to shift. The car may also creep forward when left in gear with the clutch depressed and the brakes released. This condition occurs frequently with carbon-faced throwout bearings which sometimes wear rapidly. Few

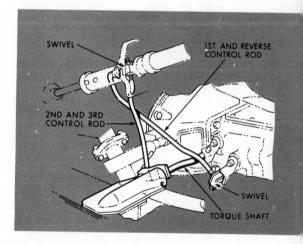

Column-mounted gear shifts can eventually develop a great deal of play due to hard use and lack of lubrication. Adjusting the swivels can correct for some of the wear.

modern cars use them, however.

Cars with hydraulic clutches, particularly popular British sport cars, often fall victim to dragging clutches or clutches

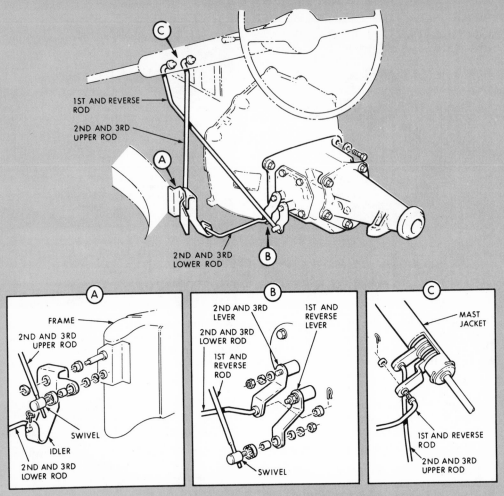

1ST AND REVERSE ROD

2ND AND 3RD UPPER ROD

A

2ND AND 3RD LOWER ROD

B

C

A

FRAME

2ND AND 3RD UPPER ROD

SWIVEL

IDLER

2ND AND 3RD LOWER ROD

B

2ND AND 3RD LEVER

1ST AND REVERSE LEVER

2ND AND 3RD LOWER ROD

1ST AND REVERSE ROD

SWIVEL

C

MAST JACKET

1ST AND REVERSE ROD

2ND AND 3RD UPPER ROD

Badly worn shift arms, rod ends and idler arms have to be replaced. Much wear can be prevented by regular lubrication. Note number of washers and bushings used.

which refuse to disengage at all. It's a joke among foreign car buffs that you can often buy a used MG for $200 less than its worth because the owner believes it needs expensive clutch work. Often all that's required are a few ounces of brake fluid in the clutch reservoir. About the most you'll need if there is an actual leak is a $2.00 cylinder rebuild kit.

Dragging hydraulic clutches may also need merely to be bled. This involves nothing more than filling the reservoir with fluid and having someone depress the clutch pedal while you open the bleed tap on the side of the slave cylinder.

When the pedal is fully depressed close the bleed tap and have the pedal released. Repeat this until fluid that doesn't contain air bubbles comes from the bleed. Top up the reservoir and you're back in business.

The mechanical linkages on domestic cars sometimes wear badly since they are exposed to road splashes and dust. This and vibration-loosened bolts may produce so much slop in the clutch linkage that the clutch cannot be disengaged completely. New parts and tightening a few bolts may do the trick and many cars have an adjustable rod between the pedal and the cross shaft which can be lengthened to correct for wear. A sagging clutch pedal that is well below the level of the brake is a good tipoff that such wear has taken place. It can also be considered a clue that a used car has received hard use or that the speedometer may have been set back if a low milage is indicated.

CHATTERING CLUTCH

There are several possible faults which may cause a clutch to chatter. Loose engine mounts are the easiest to cure. There may also be bad alignment between the transmission and engine. Torque the bolts holding the engine and transmission together and check all engine and transmission mounts carefully. Deteriorating rubber or rubber blocks which have broken their bond with the metal parts of the mount may be the trouble. Sometimes it's hard to tell whether the rubber is loose by looking at it, but if you can feel the accelerator pulsing curiously under your foot while driving it is an almost certain sign that the engine or transmission mounts are weak or broken.

A clutch disc that is binding on the splines of the transmission input shaft can also produce chattering. This condition may also be responsible for a dragging clutch. If the clutch housing has an in-

spection port (reached by removing the floorboards over the transmission) it may be possible to check for this condition visually. If the shaft is rusty an application of Liquid Wrench rust solvent will usually free the disc to slide on the shaft.

If transmission bolts are obviously loose, but tightening them does not cure the chatter completely it is likely that the misalignment has damaged the pilot bearing. This bearing is located in the center of the engine's crankshaft and receives the end of the transmission input shaft after it passes through the clutch disc.

CLUTCH REPAIR

Noisy or worn throwout bearings, worn or broken clutch discs, broken springs and oil-soaked clutch facings all mean that entensive repairs will need to be made. It is best to replace clutch parts with new or reconditioned assemblies rather than to attempt repairs on the old units.

The first step in getting at the clutch is to unbolt the driveshaft at the rear and

Typical domestic 4-speed linkage. This unit has provision in the shifter for a locating pin. With pin in place the linkage is adjusted to put gears in neutral.

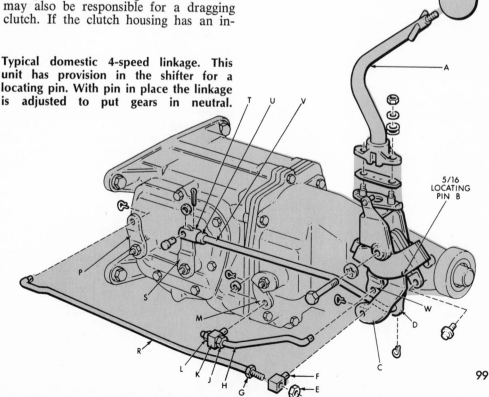

99

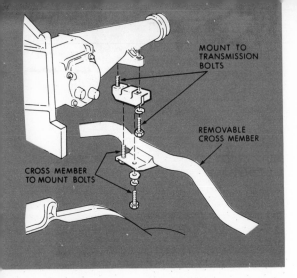

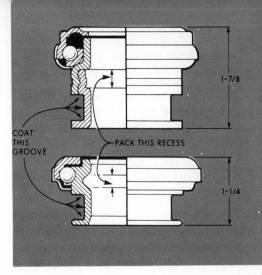

If the clutch or transmission require the replacement of any internal parts it is necessary to remove the tranmission from the car. Typical rear mount is shown here.

It could be necessary to pack the clutch throwout bearing sleeve with grease, but don't wash this part in solvent. It would destroy lube put in bearings at factory.

slide it off the back of the transmission. Place a jack or some blocks under the engine to support it and unbolt the transmission mounts. Undo the shift linkage and speedometer cable. Lower the engine (or raise the car) to drop the transmission to a low position in relation to the car's body. You'll need a transmission jack or a hefty pal to support the gearbox as you unbolt it from the flywheel bellhousing. Slide the transmission straight back until its shaft is free of the clutch and the transmission can be lowered to the floor. On VWs and other rear-engined cars you msut remove the engine to work on the clutch. The clutch domes out with engine, is easily accessible.

Remove the throwout arm and unbolt the clutch assembly from the engine's flywheel. Check the iron pressure plate for scoring and heat-bluing. Obtain a new pressure plate assembly if damage is evident. If the transmission shaft oil seal needs replacing the nose on most domestic transmissions will have to be unbolted from the gearbox. Use sealer around the outside of the new oil seal when pressing it into place. Replacement of this seal and of the throwout bearing is a good precaution against further trouble whenever a clutch is being repaired.

When installing the new clutch you'll need a tool to align the clutch disc hub with the flywheel pilot bearing. Most

home mechanics merely obtain a mainshaft from a junked transmission for this purpose. Lubricate the pilot bearing lightly with lithium grease before installing the transmission on the engine.

MANUAL TRANSMISSIONS

Transmission overhauls require special tools and equipment which make them difficult for the amateur even if he has a factory shop manual. However, many minor troubles can be corrected easily. A transmission that pops out of gear may need nothing more than to have the shift linkage adjusted. Sticking in gear or sticking between gears may also be due to worn linkages or to trouble in the transmission's side plate assembly.

Our common domestic three-speeds are the type most frequently plagued by linkage maladjustment. There are two arms on the side of the transmission sideplate. The front arm engages second gear in its forward position and high gear in the rearward position. Between these is a neutral zone. The rear arm engages first gear in its rearward position and reverse in its forward position. This arm is locked in neutral when the front arm is in high gear or second.

Check the linkage for worn parts and replace any that are found. Have a friend shift gears while you watch the arms on the side of the transmission. If they do not snap solidly into gear, remove the shift rods and adjust their length until they match the position of the transmission arms when the gears are fully engaged.

Worn shift forks and faulty neutral lockout linkages can cause a transmission to pop out of gear or jam it by engaging two gears simultaneously. The condition of these parts may be checked by draining the gearbox and removing the sideplate complete with shift forks and linkage. Used or rebuilt side plate assemblies can be obtained to replace worn units.

Sloppy floor shifts can often be returned to satisfactory condition by adjusting the pivot points or ball joints. Deteriorating cables or rubber couplings in the shift rods of rear-engined cars are another frequent cause of such trouble. Wear is the constant enemy of all transmission linkages and periodic cleaning and lubrication of the pivot points will greatly add to their lifetime.

AUTOMATICS

Not only are there a great many different types of automatic transmissions, but each type has countless variations that serve to match it to particular engine and automobile combinations. Working on an automatic requires special tools and detailed manaul for the particular car being worked on.

As with the manual transmission, a periodic check of mounting and assembly bolt torques will go a long way toward preventing trouble. Hydra-matics in particular can suffer serious damage by not being bolted tightly onto the engine. Tightening the various screws and bolts which hold the transmission case together can prevent leaks which might otherwise cause enough fluid loss to damage the transmission internally.

In addition to leaks there are a number of other common automatic transmission troubles which can be cured at home. If fluid is being forced out of the filler and the fluid level is not too high, check the following: Drain the unit and put in new fluid, water in the old oil may have been responsible for the problem. If the pan must be unscrewed to drain the transmission check the suction pipe for splits, looseness, and cracked sealing rings that

Automatic transmissions have shift links too. These can be adjusted should the selector fail to engage the right gear or if selector pointer doesn't match markings.

could allow it to suck air and cause the fluid to foam.

Be on the lookout for sludge. Old fluid which has become contaminated with water frequently fosters such a condition. If there's slow shifting and the engine surges or flares on upshifts suspect a sludged-up gearbox. The problem may even progress to the point where there is no drive at all. Clogged pickup screens and sludged valves in the pump are the cause. Removing the pan for a visual inspection and cleaning is definitely in order. A detergent additive put into the fluid a few hundred miles before a cleanout can help too. Repeated flushings of this type cost little and can often rejuvenate an automatic that might otherwise become a shop case.

SMALL ITEMS

The transmission or its linkages also control the operation of the neutral safety switch, backup light switch, and spark control switch (on late GM cars). These are among the first components that should be checked when electrical problems occur in these circuits.

The speedometer cable also drives off the transmission in most cars. The cable housing should be uncoupled from the transmission and the cable removed for periodic cleaning and lubrication. Clean the cable in kerosene, wipe it dry and coat it with speedometer cable grease. Ordinary lubricants should not be used since they may harden in winter. Cable normally serviced each 30,000 miles.

Rebuilding universal joints has its tricks. Here the old bearings are being pressed out using a big vise and socket wrenches of two different sizes. Pipe works good also.

AXLES AND U-JOINTS

You'll need a big hammer and a good strong vise for these repairs

Rubbing, grinding sounds from the rear of the car mean trouble. If they're unaffected by speed changes it's probably an axle bearing. U-joint noise is more pronounced under power and includes occasional "clanks," rattles and vibration. However, "clunks" or "clangs" that occur only as you drive off can sometimes be cured merely by torquing the bolts that hold the rear U-joint to the differential flange.

SERVICING U-JOINTS

If there's play in the U-joints themselves new bearings and seals are needed. Kits with all necessary parts can be obtained from your dealer or parts jobber. New parts are relatively cheap but repairing universal joint and rear axle bearings can still be hard work.

Raise the car and undo the driveshaft at the rear U-joint. If the car has a two-piece driveshaft unbolt the center bearing support from the chassis frame. The entire drive shaft may then be pulled rearward to slide it off the transmission and out of the car.

The bearing caps are a press fit in the U-joint yokes but they are also secured by retaining cups. Remove the retainers and select two socket wrenches, one somewhat smaller than the bearings and the other with an inside diameter slightly greater than that of the bearings. Clamp these in a vise on either side of the U-joint yoke and tighten the vise until the bearing on one side is pressed from the yoke into the larger socket. Reverse the sockets and press out the opposite bearing.

After the old bearings are out the cross can be slipped from its yoke and the process repeated to remove the other two bearings. Pry the old seals and their inner retainers off the cross, clean the parts, and press new retainers and seals into place. Replace the cross in the yoke. Coat the bearing needles with lithium grease and tap the bearing caps lightly into the yoke, driving them alternately so that the needles are not shaken out. Press in the bearing caps until the retainer grooves are uncovered just enough to accept the retainers.

Instead of the common cross and roller type universals, Chrysler Products have a ball and trunnion "pot" joint at the front end of the driveshaft. "Pot" type U-joints seldom cause trouble and are easy to service. Remove the grease cover and gasket from the mounting flange and press the "pot" back against the drive shaft. The centering buttons, washers, needle bearings and rollers may then be slid from the exposed cross pin. Don't drive out the pin unless it is damaged. Install new bearings and rollers with lithium grease and pack the pot with 1¼ ounces of grease before replacing the cover.

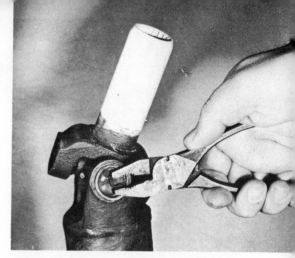

When replacing U-joint bearings the lock rings must first be removed. GM cars have rings on outside, other makes have rings installed inside universal joint yokes.

Today's U-joints are lubed for "life," although car manufacturers used to recommend that those without grease fittings be disassembled, cleaned, and repacked with grease every two years. Actually, most car owners just drive until the bearings get noisy, then install new ones. It's no harder than repacking the old ones.

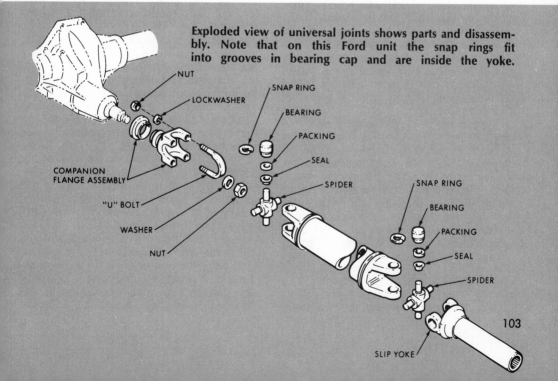

Exploded view of universal joints shows parts and disassembly. Note that on this Ford unit the snap rings fit into grooves in bearing cap and are inside the yoke.

NUT

LOCKWASHER

SNAP RING

BEARING

PACKING

SEAL

COMPANION FLANGE ASSEMBLY

SPIDER

SNAP RING

BEARING

"U" BOLT

PACKING

WASHER

SEAL

NUT

SPIDER

SLIP YOKE

103

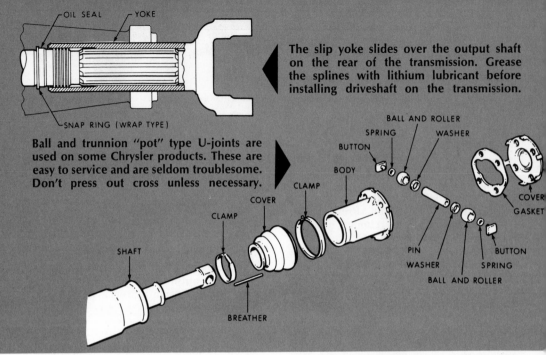

OIL SEAL — YOKE

SNAP RING (WRAP TYPE)

The slip yoke slides over the output shaft on the rear of the transmission. Grease the splines with lithium lubricant before installing driveshaft on the transmission.

Ball and trunnion "pot" type U-joints are used on some Chrysler products. These are easy to service and are seldom troublesome. Don't press out cross unless necessary.

BALL AND ROLLER
SPRING
WASHER
BUTTON
BODY
COVER
GASKET
CLAMP
COVER
CLAMP
SHAFT
PIN
WASHER
BUTTON
SPRING
BALL AND ROLLER
BREATHER

AXLE BEARINGS

Rear axle bearings are also lubed for "life," but occasionally that life is a short one. Hard driving on rough roads, heavy loads, overheated brakes, and wide-rim wheels with reversed centers are all causes of short wheel bearing life. Remove the rear wheels and brake drums when bearing trouble is suspected. If the end of the axle can be wiggled up and down it's a sure sign of bad bearings. Removing the axle retainer and brake backing plate will allow a visual inspection of the bearing. If it is blued and has baked grease around it you can be sure that there's trouble afoot.

Sometimes bearings seem alright but are causing noise due to a rough ball or race. Start the engine and place the car in "high" with the rear end jacked up. Listening for the noise at both rear wheels will tell you if one of them is causing the sound. Noises from the differential are best left to an expert for correction. However, faulty axle bearings are noisy at all speeds while gear and pinion bearing noises vary with speed and load.

AXLE REMOVAL

To replace a bad bearing or a faulty

oil seal it's necessary to remove the axle. In years past there were a variety of different axle designs which required different removal procedures. Aside from a few imports the technique is now virtually identical for all makes.

Remove the wheel and brake drum. At the center of the brake assembly you'll see the axle flange. This is a forged part of the axle and contains the wheel mounting lugs. By pulling on this flange the axle can be withdrawn complete with its bearing and retainer. Before this can be done, however, it is necessary to take off the axle retaining plate. This part is behind the axle flange and is held in place by four bolts.

A slide hammer is the correct tool for pulling an axle, but these tend to be expensive investments for one-time jobs. You can also pull an axle by attaching a length of "porch swing" chain to the wheel lugs and looping it through a cement block, an old flywheel or other heavy object. A few swift jerks will usually suffice to pull the axle free.

An automotive machine shop will remove the old bearings from the axle shaft and press the new ones on for a very low fee, but it is possible to do the work yourself. Break the old bearing race by squeezing it in a vise. Notch the old bearing hub and retainer deeply in several places with a cold chisel. Heat the retainer and bearing hub with a torch to expand them. Clamp them as lightly as possible in a vise and jerk the axle out using a slide hammer or a weight and chain. After you've done this once you'll probably be willing to take it to a machine shop next time.

OIL SEALS

The old oil seal must also come out of the axle housing. Frequently this must be replaced even when there is no bearing trouble. Any hooked object can be used for this if the opposite end can be attached to the slide hammer. The new grease seal must be pressed or driven in evenly. An old engine valve makes a good driver since one about the same diameter as the seal is easy to find.

ASSEMBLY

Don't forget to slip the axle retaining plate onto the axle before installing the new bearings. Coat the axle with trans-

This home-made slide hammer was built from a piece of scrap iron plus threaded stock, several nuts from hardware store. Cement block and chain can also work.

mission oil and slide the new bearing over it. If you have no press available, obtain a heavy length of pipe that will slip over the axle and will contact only the inner ring of the bearing. Use the pipe to hammer the bearing into place. Do the same with the new retainer after first expanding it with heat. Installing the axle is the reverse of the removal process.

As with many other repairs, disassembly and reassembly are the roughest part of the job. Even if you leave the actual replacement of U-joint and axle bearings to a machine shop there's still a worthwhile saving to be realized by doing the "dirty work" at home.

Rear axle assembly consists of many parts but replacing axle bearings and seals is the most common repair job. Bearing retainer is unbolted before pulling axle.

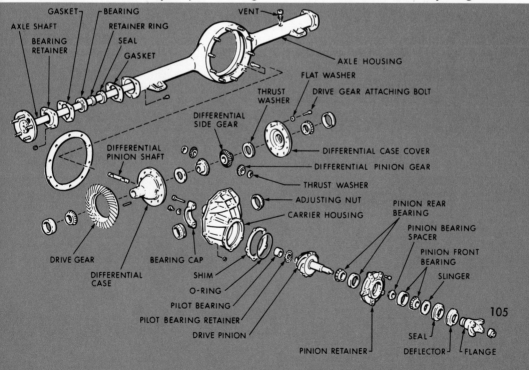

105

Installing brake linings isn't really hard, but if your car has drum brakes and the drums need to be reground, fitting the new linings should probably be left to a professional.

YOUR CAR'S BRAKES

Why wait for the brakes to fail before doing anything about them?

Driving a car with a slipping clutch may never get you into trouble but taking to the highway with sick brakes is asking for an instant case of "the deads." There's no such thing as a "sudden" brake failure. There are always plenty of warnings for those who are willing to heed them. Every car owner should make certain that the maintenance operations required to keep his car's brakes functioning safely are carried out according to schedule.

BRAKE FLUID

When the brake pedal is depressed it operates a pump called the *master cylin-*

der. This pump forces hydraulic fluid through a system of pipes and hoses to the four wheels of the car. At each wheel there are "slave" cylinders which fill with fluid as pressure from the "master" cylinder is increased. The influx of fluid forces the pistons in the wheel cylinders to move outward and press the brake linings against the wheel's rotating brake surfaces. When the driver raises his foot from the pedal springs retract the brake linings causing the wheel cylinders to force the additional fluid back into the master cylinder's reservoir.

Brake fluid tends to attract moisture from the air. This in turn causes corrosion in the brake system and sludging of the

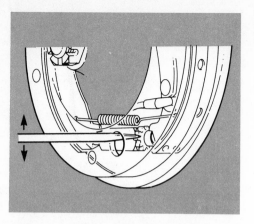

Brakes are adjusted by inserting a special tool or screwdriver and advancing a star wheel inside the drum. These may have to be backed off to remove the brake drums.

Most cars have the brake adjusting slots in the brake backing plate. Remove the rubber plug as shown and insert adjusting tool. Replace all plugs which are missing.

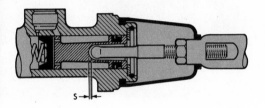

Cross section of a typical brake master cylinder shows how piston must uncover a tiny port in cylinder wall. Freeplay (S) must be about 1/10-inch to guarantee that piston can move to retracted position.

fluid. In extreme cases the water may form a concentration that significantly lowers the fluid's boiling point. If heat from the linings causes the fluid to boil there will be an almost complete loss of braking power. Air in the fluid has a similar effect. It usually enters the system through worn wheel cylinders with leaking piston seals. Swollen seals or a sludged return valve in the master cylinder will often cause the brakes to stay on even after the pedal has been released. This can wreck the entire braking system if not taken care of immediately.

All these problems can be largely prevented merely by changing the brake fluid annually or every 20,000 miles, yet no domestic car maker makes this recommendation. Builders of expensive imported cars do. Apparently their customers are more interested in keeping their cars in top-notch shape than in owning "maintenance free" transportation. A word to the wise should be sufficient!

CHANGING FLUID

Don't mix types and brands of brake fluid. When you change fluid be sure that the new juice meets the specifications established for your car.

Cars having disc brakes must be serviced with a fluid designed especially for disc brake systems.

Near where the hose enters the back of each brake assembly you'll find what appears to be a sort of grease fitting. It's not. It is the brake bleeding valve. To change the fluid, park the car in a location where spilled fluid will not be harmful. Open all four bleeding valves about two turns. Pump the brake pedal to the floor slowly several times or until most of the fluid is gone from the master cylinder reservoir. Fill the reservoir with fresh fluid and pump this out also. Repeat the process one more time, then close the bleeders and refill the reservoir. The brakes must now be bled.

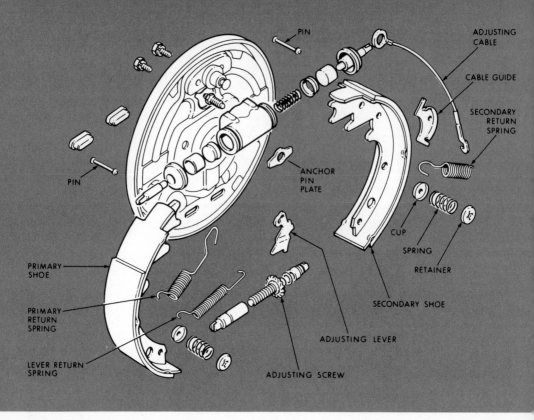

The parts of a typical drum brake assembly are shown in this drawing. Note the pins, springs, and retainers which hold the brake shoes in their places on the brake backing plate.

BLEEDING BRAKES

Brake bleeding is a job which must be done any time the hydraulic system has been opened either for repairs or to replace fluid. You'll need a helper to work the brake pedal, a length of 7/32-in. inside diameter transparent fuel tubing, and a small cup or jar to catch the fluid.

Start with the brake that is furthest away from the master cylinder. This is usually at the right rear wheel. Slip the tubing over the bleeder and place the opposite end in the jar. Open the bleed about ¼ turn and have your helper depress the pedal slowly. Fluid will be pumped into the jar. If you are bleeding the brakes following a change of fluid, keep bleeding until new fluid comes out of the tube and until no air bubbles appear. This may require several strokes of the pedal. Close the bleeder before having the pedal released, then reopening it for

the next downstroke. If you are bleeding the system following repairs continue until no air bubbles are produced.

Be sure to keep the master cylinder reservoir filled while bleeding the brakes. On cars with dual master cylinders or dual brake systems the level falls rapidly since the individual reservoirs are usually rather small. Bleed the left rear, right front, and left front brakes and the job is done. If the brakes feel "spongy" there may still be air trapped in the system. Bleed the brakes again until you are certain that the last bubble is out.

ADJUSTING

Disc brakes do not require adjusting. Most of today's drum type brakes are self-adjusting, but this feature sometimes fails to work properly. Cars having manually adjusted brakes must have their shoes advanced by hand periodically to prevent the brake pedal from getting too low. A low pedal is always a sign that brake adjustments are overdue or that they are not taking place automatically.

Some brakes are adjusted by inserting a screwdriver or brake adjusting tool through a slot in the brake backing plate. There are one or two star wheels within each brake assembly which must be rotated to move the shoes outward. Some cars, such as VW, have the adjustment opening in the face of the brake drum. Certain other cars may have a square lug projecting from the backing plate. Turning this with a wrench will advance or retract the brake shoes. Your owner's manual should show location of adjusters and indicate direction of rotation.

Self-adjusting brakes advance the star wheel each time the hand brake is used or whenever the brakes are applied with the car moving in reverse. If you never use the handbrake you may find yourself with a very low pedal. Stuck star wheels are the usual cause of failure in automatic brake adjusters.

The brake adjusters should be advanced until the shoes can be heard dragging against the drum as the tire is turned by hand. Press the brake pedal firmly to center the shoes in the drum and advance them again until they drag. When depressing the brake pedal no longer stops the shoes from dragging, advance the adjusters until it is hard to turn the wheel by hand, then back off the adjustments 1 or 2 notches or until the sound of the shoes dragging against the drum disappears.

CYLINDER REPAIRS

If the brake pedal continues to go down slowly until it finally reaches the floor there is a leak in the system. Check the hoses very carefully. Never keep a brake hose on the car which is cracked, gashed, or which has broken fabric or abrasion marks on its exterior. If no leaks are apparent, take off the brake drums and lift the rubber dust seal off each wheel cylinder. If fluid leakage is apparent the cylinder is faulty. Inspect disc

These are the integral parts of typical wheel or "slave" cylinder assemblies. Notice the shape and location of the bleeder screws. These must be loosened to bleed the brakes.

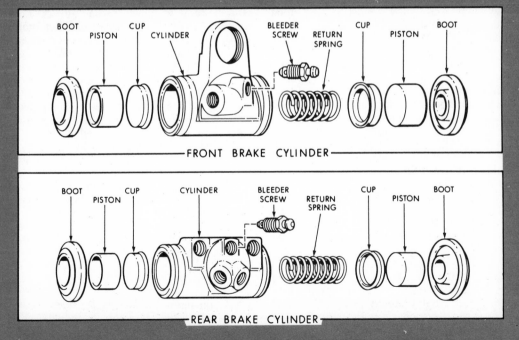

FRONT BRAKE CYLINDER

REAR BRAKE CYLINDER

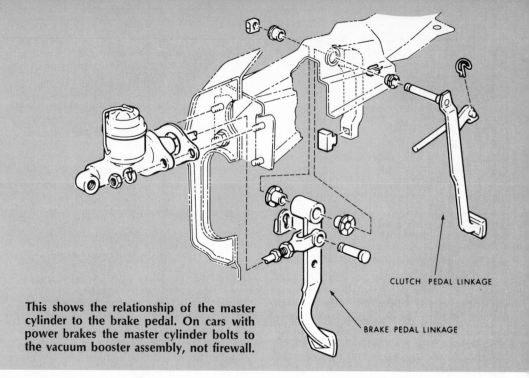

This shows the relationship of the master cylinder to the brake pedal. On cars with power brakes the master cylinder bolts to the vacuum booster assembly, not firewall.

CLUTCH PEDAL LINKAGE

BRAKE PEDAL LINKAGE

brake calipers for signs of leaking fluid.

Usually, however, the above mentioned symptoms indicate a faulty master cylinder. If the car has over 50,000 miles on it it's usually best to merely install a replacement master cylinder since the cylinder walls may be worn past their useful life in the old unit. On low mileage cars it's economically sound to rebuild the master cylinder.

Obtain a rebuild kit and a brake cylinder hone. Remove the master cylinder from the firewell or from the power brake vacuum booster. Withdraw the piston and lay the various internal parts out on a clean tabel in the order and position in which they were removed. Inspect the cylinder for pits and scoring and hone the cylinder until these disappear. Oversize rebuild kits are available to make up for the honing, but .005″ is the practical limit before declaring it a lost cause. Clean and deburr the small holes in the cylinder walls and blow out all abrasive dust after honing.

Wash brake parts with brake fluid or pure denatured alcohol. If the rubber seals appear swollen and spongy the fluid has been contaminated with fuel, oil, or kerosene. In such cases the entire system should be flushed out with 188-195 proof denatured alcohol and the wheel cylinder piston seals inspected for similar deterioration before putting in clean fluid.

Lubricate the piston seals with brake fluid as you install them in the cylinder. It's helpful to have a diagram of the cylinder to guide its reassembly, but such a drawing is included with most non-factory rebuild kits. When installing the master cylinder make certain that there is at least 1/10th″ of freeplay between the push rod coming from the pedal or vacuum booster and the master cylinder piston. A shop manual can provide accurate specifications for your particular car.

Wheel cylinders should be inspected for leakage periodically by lifting their dust covers. If faulty they can be rebuilt or replaced. New brake lines can also be obtained to replace any that show serious corrosion damage or dents caused by flying stones. The brakes must always be bled following any of the repairs described above.

DISC BRAKE LININGS

If you have disc brakes consider yourself lucky. It's possible to inspect the thickness of the linings without taking anything apart and replacing worn linings is a job that takes barely minutes. Some car makers recommend that the discs be replaced at every second pad change. However, many machine shops are now equipped to resurface the discs. Unless seriously scored they can be made to last the life of the car.

To replace the pads (linings) on disc brakes, take off the wheel and tire, then remove the anti-rattle spring clip or the retaining pins that lock the pads in the caliper. Insert a stiff wire hook through the opening in each brake pad's backing plate and pull the pads from the caliper. There are also thin metal shims that must come out. Replacements for these are included with the new linings.

Never depress the brake pedal while the pads are out. Wash away any dirt around the pistons with brake fluid and have the discs ground if they are scored deeply enough to make withdrawing the pads difficult. You'll have to unbolt the calipers and take the wheel spindle nuts off the front wheels to remove the discs, so be careful not to lose the wheel bearings. Rear discs normally slide off the axle flange after removing retaining screw.

The brake pistons will have to be pushed back into the caliper slightly to permit the new, thicker pads to slide in. A putty knife is a handy tool for this, but it's wise to remove some of the fluid from the master cylinder to prevent overflowing as the pistons are pushed in. Be sure to install the shims and pads so that any arrows marked on them are pointed in the direction of forward wheel rotation.

DRUM BRAKE LININGS

Drum brakes are very temperamental about the fit of their linings and on high-mileage cars or those with worn and scored drums the entire job is best turned over to a brake shop. Drums which have been scored by metal-to-metal contact with brake shoes or rivets will need to be resurfaced. This alone should provide the motivation to check lining thickness each 10,000 miles. If the linings are worn to within .002″ of the rivets or if total lining thickness is 1/16″ or less, replace linings.

Drums also need resurfacing if they are

When rebuilding a brake cylinder the first step is to take it apart and inspect the damage. Master cylinder has snap ring to remove but wheel cylinders usually do not.

This is a typical master cylinder rebuild kit. Notice that diagram of the cylinder is shown on instruction sheet. Oversize pistons are available for worn cylinders.

A brake cylinder hone is needed to remove scoring and pitting from inside the brake cylinder. A variable-speed power drill is the best tool for driving a cylinder hone.

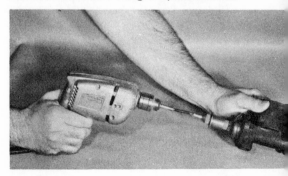

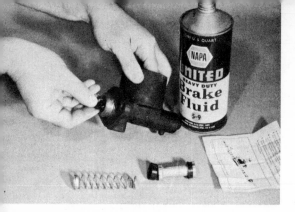

After honing clean the cylinder and lube the new parts with brake fluid before you install them. Never clean or lubricate brake parts with petroleum greases or oil.

Removal and replacement of disc brake pads is a very simple operation. Pull out the lock clips and withdraw the pins that hold the brake lining pads and shims in place.

Once the retaining pins are out the thin backing shims and the brake pads can be withdrawn from the brake caliper. Do this when removing the caliper assembly also.

bellmouthed (often caused by overheating), out of round, or if normal wear has recessed the friction area more than about .005″. The man at the machine shop can tell you whether it's possible to recondition them or not. Reconditioned drums are slightly oversize, which means that their radius will not be quite the same as that of the new brake shoes. Special machinery is needed to grind the shoes to the new radius, so when drums are badly worn it's best to leave the whole job to a well equipped brake specialist.

Nowadays it's usually possible to trade in your old brake shoes for new ones with the linings already installed. There's a special lever-like tool used to pry off the retracting springs that link the two brake shoes of each wheel together and this item is well worth purchasing. Small cars, however, have light springs which can usually be removed by hand or with the help of a screwdriver.

The shoe retainer springs must also be removed. This is done by placing one finger behind the brake backing plate to hold the retaining pin in, then pushing on the retainer to compress the spring. Turn the retainer until the slots line up with the flattened end of the pin and the retainer and spring will come off, releasing the brake shoe.

Clean all dust from the brake parts with a stiff brush before installing the new linings. Never touch the linings or drums with greasy hands. Coat the areas of the backing plate against which the shoes rest with Lubriplate. Lubriplate may also be used to lubricate the adjusters and hand brake linkage. The brake adjustments must always be backed off when new linings are installed or the drums will not go on. Adjust the brakes after the drums are once again in place. If the car has automatic adjusters this can be done by moving the car in reverse and applying the brakes repeatedly.

Thanks to bonded linings, disc brakes, improved designs, and government standards for brake fluid, braking systems are becoming much more trouble-free and easier to service than they were in the past. If the fluid is kept clean and adjustments are made regularly, one or two changes of linings should be the only repair work required in 100,000 miles of driving with today's automobiles.

Installing a brand new exhaust system isn't nearly as hard as getting the old one off. The key to a successful job is getting everything lined up carefully so it doesn't rattle.

THE EXHAUST SYSTEM

Replacing mufflers and tailpipes takes more muscles than know-how

At least a gallon of water pours into the exhaust system for every gallon of gasoline your car burns. Exhaust gasses also contain sulphuric acid and other corrosive agents, so it's not surprising that mufflers and exhaust pipes frequently become riddled with holes in a relatively short time.

INSPECTION AND REMOVAL

If the exhaust seems noisy, place your hand over the end of the tailpipe with the engine running. If there are loud hisses from under the car, but the engine does not slow down, you probably have at least one hole in the system. Replace exhaust system components, don't try to fix them. "Spot" repairs are a good way to convert

your car into a rolling gas chamber.

Replace the muffler and tail pipe at the same time. If one has acquired holes the other is never far behind. Also, do both sides of dual exhaust systems. Head and crossover pipes are made of better steel and stay hot enough to evaporate moisture. They'll usually outlast at least two mufflers.

If you enjoy beating your wife you'll love exhaust system removal. It takes a big hammer, a wrench set, a hacksaw with a round tungsten carbide blade, and a couple of chisels. An ordinary cold chisel is alright, but a diamond point chisel is better and a "T"-shaped muffler spitter is best.

Raise the car off the ground by backing it onto a pair of wheel ramps or place

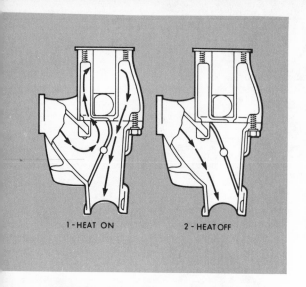

1 - HEAT ON   2 - HEAT OFF

Heat riser valves have been a headache for generations. More and more cars have gone to water-heated manifolds because of this. Keep valve moving freely, lube it often.

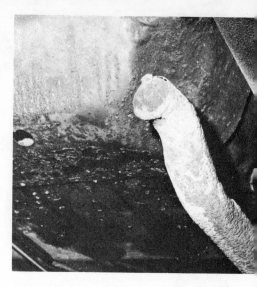

Here is the making of a disaster. Drain plug is missing from trunk floor and the exhaust pipe has broken off nearby. This car is a first-class rolling gas chamber!

it on 4 jack stands. If you're not going to save the head pipe saw it off ahead of the muffler. If you want to keep it in one piece remove the muffler clamp and split the muffler inlet pipe with a chisel or muffler splitter. Be careful not to damage the head pipe. When you reach the end of the head pipe pry under the cut to loosen the muffler. Now take off the clamps and hangers supporting the muffler and tail pipe and hammer the muffler off off the head pipe. You may now drag the muffler and tail pipe out from under the car.

Tap the head pipe and V-8 engine crossover pipes lightly with the hammer. If they have a nice ring it's safe to reuse them. A dull sound means cracks and corroded metal.

THE NEW PARTS

Always state whether your car has automatic transmission, power steering, and whether it is a convertible, sedan, or station wagon when ordering or purchasing new exhaust system components. These

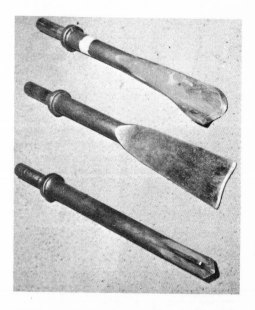

Tools like these are used to cut old pipes and mufflers from car. Lower "T" chisel is for splitting pipes, top chisel is used to peel rusted exhaust system joints apart.

114

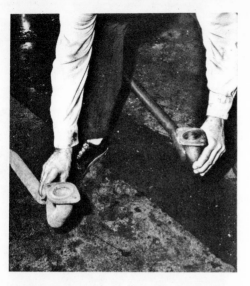

Hang the muffler and all pipes in place but do not tighten any of the clamps until the components in the system have all been aligned properly with car and each other.

Compare the new pipe and muffler to those which came off the car. Small differences sometimes exist between convertibles and sedans, cars with sticks and automatics.

things often affect pipe routing and call for different parts. Use new clamps and gaskets and replace the hangers if they're in poor condition.

Install the new parts but do not clamp them together until everything is loosely in place. Align the pipes and mufflers carefully so that they do not make contact with the body, frame, brake cables, shock absorbers or any other part of the car. Once aligned they may be clamped together solidly. Check for rattles and leaks. If you find any correct them immediately since it's almost impossible to shift the position of the parts even after only a few days of corrosion.

HEAT VALVES

The heat riser valves located inside the exhaust manifolds of some engines have a nasty way of rusting in place. Water-heated intake manifolds are gradually replacing these, but if your car has one it's visible as a shaft with a (hopefully) movable weight and a flat spiral spring. Make sure it always moves freely and treat it periodically with heat valve anti-seize lubricant.

A sound exhaust system is beneficial to your health as well as to your car. Skip the goo, stickum and patented patches. If you want to save money do it by obtaining the new parts from a low-cost source such as Sears and by handling the installation job yourself.

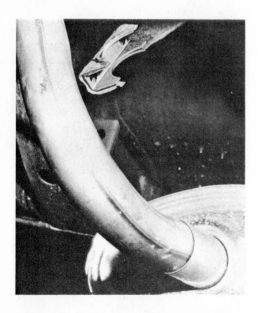

Rust weakened exhaust pipe hangers can be beefed up for further use by slipping the cross-bar of a new muffler clamp inside them. Replacements are also available.

TIRES AND SUSPENSION

How to help your automobile

over a case of the shakes and shivers

Every year hundreds of cars fail to pass state inspections because of loose front ends. Exactly how many accidents have been caused by worn shock absorbers, faulty tires and sloppy steering nobody can say. No one, however, will deny that these factors constitute one of the hardest-to-police aspects of highway safety. Whether your car is brand new, almost new, or a veteran of many years service it's never too early to too late to give attention to the things that help it keep all four wheels rolling smoothly on the road.

TIRES

When you see tires advertised as "equal to new-car equipment" it's not saying much. Before Federal law required tire makers to list the load capacity on the sidewalls of tires abuse of the consumer was often terrible. Even now the "standard" tires offered by the factory are nothing to write home about. One of the first things you can do to guarantee yourself a safer, better handling car is to order the best tire option available on your new car. Leave off the freaky wheel covers and skip the electric seat warmers, but don't skimp when it comes to the rubber on the road.

After you get your new car take it to a good wheel and alignment shop and have them check the tire balance and make sure that the wheels are pointing in the right direction. Dealer preparation is shamefully lax in this area and unless everything is right from the very beginning you'll be unable to obtain the mileage from your tires that was designed into them.

Buying replacement tires seems to have been rendered purposely risky by many tire makers. Grand sounding brand names such as "Safety All Terrain" are given even to their cheapest, most poorly constructed lines. Comparing prices doesn't help much either since the retail mark-up is so huge and so flexible that dealers are sometimes able to bilk the unknowing customer out of a king's ran-

Some phases of tire and suspension work must be left to an expert, such as wheel balancing and alignment. The car owner, however, can perform some of the maintenance work.

som for a tire near the bottom of the manufacturer's service scale.

Shop until you find a dealer who will show you literature from the manufacturer which accurately describes where the tires you are considering fit into his lineup. Above all, stay away from "cheapies" with unfamiliar brand names that are sold in discount stores. Some of these will wear out on a quick trip around the block and their so-called guarantees are usually about as worthless as a well-known type of paper that comes in long rolls on short cardboard tubes.

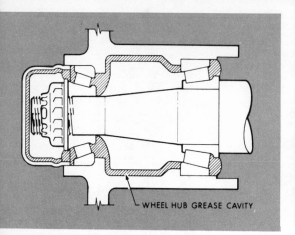

WHEEL HUB GREASE CAVITY

Repacking and adjusting the front wheel bearings is a simple task that can easily be done by the owner. Shaded area shows where grease must be applied to hub.

The brake caliper must be removed from cars with disc brakes to service the wheel bearings. Installation and adjustment are jobs identical to other cars, however.

The wheel bearings must be taken out as is shown here for washing, careful inspection and a thorough packing with fresh grease. Adjustment steps are shown at the bottom.

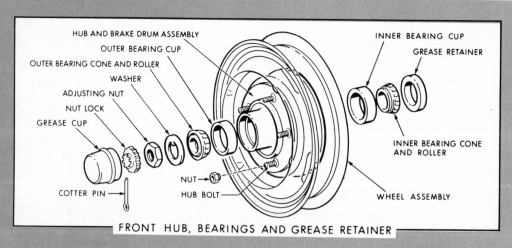

HUB AND BRAKE DRUM ASSEMBLY
OUTER BEARING CUP
OUTER BEARING CONE AND ROLLER
WASHER
ADJUSTING NUT
NUT LOCK
GREASE CUP
COTTER PIN
NUT
HUB BOLT

INNER BEARING CUP
GREASE RETAINER
INNER BEARING CONE AND ROLLER
WHEEL ASSEMBLY

FRONT HUB, BEARINGS AND GREASE RETAINER

WITH DRUM AND WHEEL ROTATING, TORQUE THE ADJUSTING NUT TO 17-25 FT. LBS.

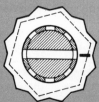

INSTALL LOCK ON NUT SO THAT CASTELLATIONS ARE ALIGNED WITH COTTER PIN HOLE.

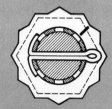

BACK OFF NUT AND NUT LOCK ONE CASTELLATION. INSTALL COTTER PIN.

TIRE REPAIRS

There's no cure for a tire with separated plys, a chunking tread, or split sidewall. The guarantees on better tires may cover such damage, however. Punctures can be fixed, but the plug-type quick repairs performed in service stations while the tire mounted on the wheel are something that should be outlawed. The Rubber Manufacturers Association warns that such repairs should be considered *temporary emergency fixes only*. Safe repairs can only be made by placing a vulcanized patch on the inside of the tire.

Retread tires are a mixed bag from the quality standpoint. True, retreading can be a low-cost way of converting your worn standard tires into usable snow tires and for keeping your "around town" car shod at minimum expense. But that retreads often come apart at highway speeds can be verified merely by taking a short drive along any Interstate. The number of thrown treads lying along the berm give mute testimony to the retread's greatest failing.

The cheaper retreads may also prove impossible to balance and their treads may not be placed evenly on the tire carcass. Unless you enjoy having your palms massaged by the steering wheel, skip the $8.88 "bargains" and obtain your retreaded tires from factory-backed dealers.

SHOCK ABSORBERS

Next to out-of balance tires, weak shock absorbers are probably the most common wheel and suspension problem requiring the driver's attention. Tire balance should be re-checked at least every 10,000 or 12,000 miles and it's a good idea to have the front end alignment checked at the same time. Unfortunately, failing shock absorbers are often overlooked at these check-ups. The fact is, many standard new-car shocks are almost shot by the time that first 12,000 miles rolls around.

Inspect the shock absorbers for leaks by jacking up your car until the shock absorber piston rods are visible. If there's a dark-colored wet stain surrounding the opening where the rod passes through the

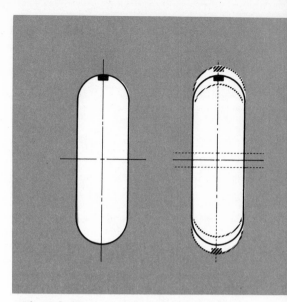

Wheel balance is extremely important to proper tire life. Heavy spots on one side of wheel are easily corrected by static balancing at service station or tire shop.

Static balancing cannot correct this kind of imbalance. Heavy spots in different areas on opposite side of tire's center line call for dynamic balancing methods.

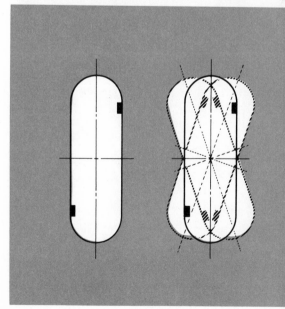

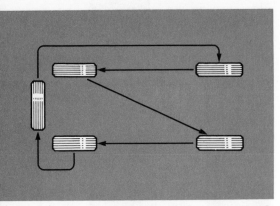

Tire rotation can spread the wear evenly over all five tires. This means that the whole set can be replaced at the same time and that handling will always be uniform.

Wet stains around the shock absorber's rod indicate that the unit is leaking fluid. This is always the beginning of the end and means shocks should be replaced soon.

cylinder the shock is leaking and its useful days are numbered. Bouncing the car is another classic test for worn shocks. Hop up and down on the bumper until the car is rocking vigorously, then jump off. If the car keeps rocking instead of rebounding once and settling into its normal attitude the shocks are weak.

Garages and service stations make a fantastic profit installing shock absorbers because they're able to buy replacement shocks from jobbers at a much lower price than you'd have to pay. The catch is that they'll usually charge you the same price for the parts that you'd have paid at the jobber's. There's nothing to installing new shock absorbers except taking off the old ones and bolting in the new ones into place. Any car owner should be able to perform the task without trouble. However, your greatest saving comes from finding replacement shocks at the lowest possible price.

Sears, Montgomery Ward and Penneys all offer excellent shock absorbers at lower prices than you're likely to pay for replacements from most other sources. Even lower prices are available from various automotive mail order houses, but always choose from their "heavy duty" lines. Some of the real "cheapies" aren't much better than worn out factory shocks.

WHEEL BEARINGS

When the state inspector lifts the front of your car and shakes the front wheels he's looking for looseness. He probably won't tell you exactly what the trouble is, and if you leave the car with him for repairs or take it to an independent garage you may end up paying a healthy sum for a very minor adjustment.

Loose front wheel bearings are the most frequent reason why cars fail to pass state front-end checks. It's a condition which can usually be corrected merely by removing the dust cover from the center of the wheel and tightening the nut that holds the wheel onto the spindle. There's a definite technique to this, and since repacking the front wheel bearings is a part of routine maintenance we'll cover this operation before getting into the actual adjustment procedure.

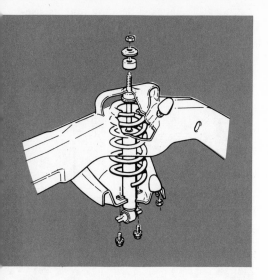

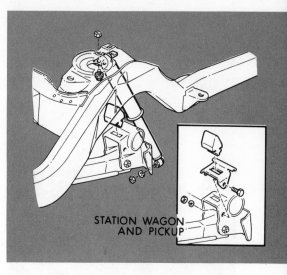

STATION WAGON
AND PICKUP

Typical installation of a front shock unit is shown here. New rubber bushings and suspension stops should be installed at the same time for like-new ride, handling.

Rear shock absorber installation differs only slightly from method used at front. Top of shock is freed from inside the trunk on some cars. Penetrating oil is big help.

The wheel bearings should be checked for proper adjustment each 12,000 miles. Most car makers require that the bearings be repacked with fresh grease each 24,000 or 30,000 miles—although it may be less. The grease must be a type specifically designated for use in wheel bearings. It may not be called wheel bearing grease, although it sometimes is, but it will definitely state somewhere on the can that it is suitable for this purpose. In addition to a half-pound can of grease you'll need some kerosene for washing the bearings new cotter pins for the spindle nut, and new grease seals for the inside of the hub. Some may consider this last item optional, but it's usually impossible to remove the inner bearings for cleaning without taking out the old seal and the cost of the seals is usually less than a dollar.

REPACKING

Pry off the dust cover and remove the cotter pin from the wheel spindle. If the car has disc brakes it is also necessary to unbolt the brake caliper. Slide the caliper off the disc and support it with a wire hook so that the weight of the unit will not be placed on the brake hose. Remove the spindle nut lock and screw the spindle nut off the spindle. Older VWs have a lock nut which must be removed before taking off the adjusting nut, but on late models there is a crossbolt through one side of a clamp-type adjusting nut. This must be loosened to get the nut off the spindle.

After the nut and thrust washer have been removed the brake disc (or drum) can be pulled from the spindle. Be ready to catch the outer bearings in case they fall out. Remove the outer bearings and place them carefully in a pan of kerosene. Wipe the old grease from the wheel spindle and inspect the condition of its bearing surfaces. Should either be roughened or heat blued they must be replaced. This job requires different tools and techniques for different cars so it's best to consult a shop manual. Pry the grease seal out of the back of the wheel hub. Carefully remove the rear bearings and place them in the pan of kerosene.

Wash the bearings gently and inspect them carefully for damage. The slightest sign of wear or roughness means that replacement is necessary. Lay the bearings

Many drivers who travel rough roads, tow trailers or carry heavy loads have found that air lifts give big improvement. Air bag slips into the rear spring, is inflated.

Top of front shock absorber must usually be loosened from under the hood. Some cars also have wheel alignment adjustments at this point, so loosen only shock bolts.

aside to dry on a soft cloth and wash the spindle nuts and thrust washers. Next, wash out the inside of the wheel hub. Be very thorough about this and dry the inside carefully. Inspect the bearing surfaces inside the hub. If they are damaged a machine shop can install new ones.

Place a small quantity of grease in the palm of your hand and thrust the inner bearing repeatedly into it with a rubbing motion until the balls or rollers are thoroughly coated with lubricant. Coat the inner bearing race of the wheel with grease and place the lubricated bearing on top of it. Carefully drive the new grease seal into its recess, starting it by hand and seating it with a flat block of wood and light blows from a hammer.

Turn the wheel over and fill the hub cavity with about ⅛ pound of grease. Never fill the hub completely since this might cause expansion to force grease past the seal and spoil the brake linings. Give the wheel spindle a light coat of grease and slip the wheel onto it, being careful to guide the grease seal and bearings smoothly into place. Lubricate the outer bearing just as you did the inner

one and slip it over the spindle and into the hub. Install the thrust washer and adjusting nut.

ADJUSTMENT

Old timers used to spin the tire and adjust the wheel bearings by feel. Disc brakes have spelled the end of such haphazard methods since their constant drag makes it impossible to tell whether or not the bearings are being overtightened. Overtightening can ruin the bearings instantly, so the following method is advisable for all cars with roller type bearings, and especially those with discs.

Fit a torque wrench to the bearing adjustment nut. Spin the wheel counterclockwise while gently tightening the adjusting nut. Continue slow and smoothly until a torque reading of 25-27 foot-pounds is reached. Fit the locking devices and cotter pins to the spindle and replace the dust cover. Few recent cars other than pre-1966 Volkswagens have ball bearings at the front end. The bearings on these VWs are considered to be in proper adjustment when the flat washer behind the adjusting nut may just bare-

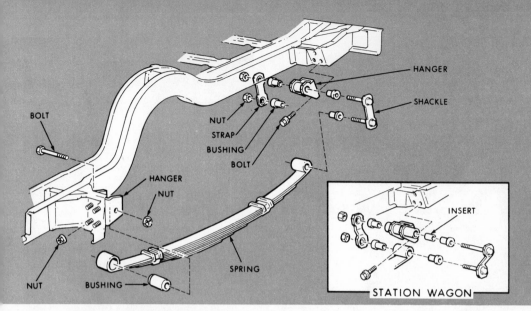

When the suspension bushings become worn the car handles very badly and gives a harsh, noisy ride. Replacing the bolts and bushings can restore condition of rear suspension.

Play in the steering gear box can usually be adjusted out. Loosen lock nut on the clearance adjusting screw. Tighten screw until resistance is felt, tighten lock nut.

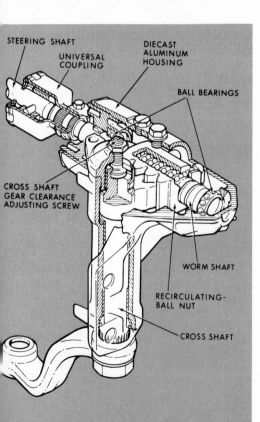

ly be shifted from side to side by pressing against its edge with a screwdriver.

LOOSE STEERING

Steering play can be corrected by making adjustments at the steering gear box. However, each individual steering system design requires different procedures and these are best obtained from a shop manual written for the particular make and model car you are working on. Worn tie rod ends and suspension ball joints are not adjustable and must be replaced. Since their installation must be followed by accurate wheel alignment work it is advisable to leave such work to a well-equipped garage.

Periodic shock absorber checks, a careful tire inspection at each tune-up and regular tire balancing and wheel alignment checks are the key to owning a safer, better handling car. Wheel bearings that are kept in adjustment and packed with clean grease will outlive the car. Those that are neglected may fail before you've made the last payment on your new car. They could even cause a wheel to fall off. So, when it comes to wheel bearings, it's definitely not advisable to "just keep driving 'til something goes wrong."

The philosophy of the small car is to make the machinery compact and light to leave as much room for people and packages as is possible. The car shown loads from both ends.

YOUR SMALL CAR

Your simplified four or six cylinder power plant is easier to fix

Car owners who want to do their own maintenance and repair work as possible must choose a car which will allow them to do it. This has been one of the appealing features of the more successful imported cars for many years. As much as the advertising industry might hate to admit it, it has also been one of the considerations that has kept six-cylinder cars in steady demand right through the era dominated by the more glamorous V-8.

Easy, low cost home servicing has been an obvious goal in the design of several domestic small cars. Their four cylinder

powerplants are far less intimidating to the home mechanic than a monsterous V-8 that's been stuffed into an engine compartment that's barely big enough to receive it. Perhaps the best indication that the auto industry has at last faced up to the fact that many potential car buyers would rather "do it themselves" is the excellent "Do-It-Yourself Service Manual" offered by General Motors for "Vega" owners. This 112 page, $1.25 book (GM Part No. 3988975) covers all common operations with a thoroughness that was formerly reserved for shop manuals.

The "Vega" itself has a full complement of grease fittings, a drain plug for the automatic transmission and many other features which mark it as a "natural" for the home mechanic. In addition to covering such important jobs as changing shock absorbers and carrying out brake work, the "Vega" Do It Yourself book tells what tools and parts are needed for each job and contains such interesting and helpful tips as How To Use a turkey baster and a three-foot length of 7/32" I.D. fuel hose to add oil to the manual transmission and rear axle.

LIGHT METALS

Small cars with inline engines are easier to work on, but they also require special finesse. Cast iron, the notorious "Pittsburgh plaster" of the auto industry, is seldom lavished on small cars in the way it is on their larger cousins. The idea of a small car is basically this: Keep mechanical components small to leave more room for people and packages, then make the car small and light so it won't overtax the machinery. Thin wall casting techniques keep cast iron parts to minimum weight and aluminum or magnesium alloy replaces many parts formerly made from iron. Volkswagen, for example, consumes more magnesium than the combined aerospace industry of the entire world!

Because light materials and smaller bolt sizes are used in small cars it is essential to use a torque wrench for virtually all mechanical work. Bolts threaded into aluminum or magnesium should always be coated with antiseize to prevent the threads in the light metal from being ruined. This is something which must be remembered whether you are putting spark plugs in your VW or installing a new water pump on a "Vega."

FOREIGN FASTENERS

Many drivers who are considering a smaller car are frightened by the thought that imported machinery requires special tools. Actually, Whetworth hex sizes have completely disappeared from English cars, elthough Whetworth threads still persist on some makes. English cars now have bolt heads identical to U.S. sizes.

Lightweight 4-cylinder engines are easy to lift onto workbench for repairs, use low-cost parts. However, a torque wrench is a must to avoid damage during assembly.

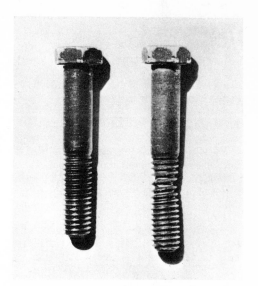

Stretched Ford Pinto rocker arm shaft bolt shows what can happen when ham-handed back yard mechanics try to work on small car engines without following torque specs.

All European and most Japanese cars employ metric bolts. These should be handled with metric wrenches. However, most manufacturers use 13-mm hex size nuts and bolts in those areas where routine service is required since a 13-mm wrench is identical to an American ½" wrench. Usually, a great many other fas-

At 50¢, a new VW front wheel grease seal costs about half price of a similar part for other cars. This is a good example of savings possible in the servicing of a small car.

teners are also metric sizes which approximate popular U.S. equivalents. However, the fit of U.S. wrenches still tends to be excessively tight or sloppy.

FINDING PARTS

Parts for domestic small cars are no harder to obtain than parts for any other American automobile. Unfortunately, this often means a lengthy delay. Volkswagen dealers are usually able to supply parts out of stock, but the situation with other makes is too often "You'll have to wait while we order it." It's been one of the keys to "The Bug's" success. If you're going to have to wait for parts to be ordered, why not order them yourself from a source that isn't going to overcharge you as most dealers do?

J.C. Whitney & Co. (1917-19 Archer Ave., Chicago, Ill. 60616) not only lists a great many foreign car parts in its regular mail order catalog but also has a separate catalog especially for imported cars. Sears has two mail order catalogs which are of interest to the imported car owner. One is devoted completely to foreign cars and the other also includes custom and performance items in addition to parts for U.S. cars, trucks, Jeep-type vehicles and dune buggies. These companies stock

parts for domestic cars too—all at reasonable prices.

BAP/Geon, which has a dealership network in major cities from coast to coast, can supply virtually any part for any foreign car. Local jobbers and parts stores throughout the country have tune-up components, oil filters and exhaust system components for the more popular imports, so give them a try before throwing yourself on the mercy of a car dealer. Perhaps the best advice for those who are buying a low-volume import and whose dealer may be some distance away is to lay in a supply of spares.

An extra fan belt is a must. An engine gasket set, brake and clutch cylinder repair kits, extra wheel bearings (front and rear) oil seals, radiator hoses, distributor cap, and possibly even a used starter, generator, and voltage regulator are a good starting point for owners of "exotic" imports who had to buy their car from a dealer ninety miles away in the State Capitol.

PROBLEM AREAS

Small cars have always had a couple of problem areas associated with them. Those with high-revving engines or which must operate at or near full throttle to keep up with traffic are likely to need valve grings more often than big, slow-turning V-8s. Richer carburetor jets will help on those engines which are "screwed down" for economy, but don't ask what this might do for our precious clean air. Keeping the valves in proper adjustment is a must, and setting them .001" or .002" wider than specs can help on some engines.

One of the best ways to improve valve life is simply to lap the valves into their seats after grinding them. Keep the seats narrowed to specifications, grind both valve and seat to 45° and lap them in. Some "experts" might not agree with this, but it works. Also, make sure that there is enough oil getting to the valves. Try leaving the valve stem seals off your VW.

Another common problem area is spark plugs. Some small car engines never have plug trouble while others eat electrodes like a hungry drunk gobbles free pretzels. Many foreign car owners have

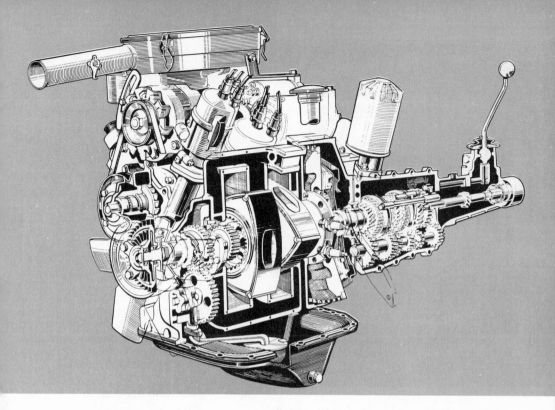

CROSS SECTION OF MAZDA R100 COUPE ENGINE

Rotary engines are beginning to appear in small cars from Japan, Germany and France. Service and tune-up work, however, is not unlike maintenance required by any other auto.

found that changing to the Japanese NGK copper-core plugs or to one of Champion's projected-nose *racing* plugs will effect a cure. Don't replace resistance-type plug cables with metallic conductor cables. This can cause spark erosion that's severe enough to kill the plugs all by itself.

ROTARY ENGINES

The Wankel-derived rotary engine is now appearing in a number of small cars, two of which are being imported into the U.S. This type of powerplant is likely to be seen in even more cars in the future, perhaps even in Detroit products.

The important thing to remember about servicing the rotary is that it's not so different from the common piston en-

gine as you might first suspect. The distributors, carburetor, water pump, starter, alternator and all other components requiring routine maintenance are identical to those found on any other gasoline powered vehicle. The same timing light you use on your Ford Fairlane will work just as well on a Mazda R-100 rotary.

FUEL INJECTION

The best advice for owners of cars with mechanical fuel injection systems is don't tamper with it. A new Bosch pump for your Mercedes will cost almost $600, so if anybody is going to bust it, let it be the dealer's mechanic.

Electronic fuel injection set-ups such as those used in Volkswagen, SAAB and

Constant vacuum carbs like this Stromberg are found on many small imports. Cap must be removed from the top for the addition of S.A.E. Twenty oil at each service interval.

quire at least one phase of maintenance that other carburetors do not. This is keeping the piston damper filled with S.A.E. 20 motor oil. They really *are* carburetors, even though U.S. mechanics are usually terrified by them. Adjustments are performed in a manner that's little different from that used with any other carburetor. But because there are so many different types and models in circulation it is best to consult a manual for your car to determine the location of the adjusting screws.

OVERHEAD CAMS

With the advent of the Pinto 2000 and the Chevy Vega overhead cams have finally come to America. (They've been around for years on imports.) Adjusting the valve clearances on something like a Jaguar is a long and impossibly involved job. Even the Lotus Twin Cam must have its camshafts removed for a change of shims when adjustments are needed.

Fortunately, the OHC engines on the more popular imports and on U.S. small cars are quite easily adjusted. To set the Vega's valves (.015″ intake .030″ exhaust) requires only a 3⁄8″ socket, feeler gauges, and a 1⁄8″ Allen wrench. The Allen wrench is inserted in the valve lifter to turn the adjusting screw. This operation is detailed fully in the "Vega" Do-It-Yourself manual.

The overhead cam engine used in the Ford Pinto and in Lincoln-Mercury's Capri 2000 has rocker arms which are operated by the camshaft in a manner similar to that used for years by Mercedes-Benz. There is an adjusting hex beneath the ball-joint end of the rocker arm which is turned with an ordinary 1⁄2″ wrench to effect adjustments. The feeler gauge should be placed between the valve stem and rocker arm as any push-rod OHV engine.

When it comes to maintenance the small car owner is indeed fortunate. Even washing and waxing it takes far less time and effort, and when an outfit like GM decides that they should encourage the home mechanic it may be time even for skeptics to admit that the era of the shade tree mechanic has never really ended in America.

Volvo rely on a computer. (Also known as the "black box" even though it's really silver.) *Leave the box alone*, but keep the terminals serving it and those on all wires associated with the injection system spotlessly clean. A good going over with crocus cloth at each tune-up isn't too much to ask. Even a voltage drop of less than one volt may cause the unit to function erratically. If the injection system keeps blowing fuses there's probably a grounded wire to be found. Also, be careful to keep a sound high tension cable on the VW's ignition since it lies parallel to one of the injector leads and leaking insulation will allow a spark to arc across to the injector wire.

IT'S A CARBURETOR

The Su, Hitachi and Stromberg constant depression carburetors found on certain British, Japanese and Swedish cars re-

INDEX

Key:

Chapter heads are in capital letters

Bold face numerals indicate a photo

Italicized numerals indicate diagram